CLEAN FOOD SOURCE

A Complete Guide To Successful Aquaponic Gardening

BY OLI FISCHER

DISCLAIMER

The information presented herein represents the view of the author as of the date of publication. Because of the rate with which conditions change, the author reserves the right to alter and update his opinion based on the new conditions. The report is for informational purposes only.

While every attempt has been made to verify the information provided in this report, neither the author nor his affiliates or partners assume any responsibility for errors, inaccuracies or omissions. Any slights of people or organizations are unintentional.

The Purchaser or Reader of this publication assumes responsibility for the use of these materials and information. The Author and Publisher assume no responsibility or liability whatsoever on the behalf of any Purchaser or Reader of these materials.

COPYRIGHT

Images courtesy of iStockphoto

TABLE OF CONTENTS

IV. SCOPING YOUR SYSTEM

V. DESIGNING YOUR SYSTEM

VIII. MAINTAINING YOUR SYSTEM

IX. FOOD HARVESTING

X. FINAL AQUAPONIC WORDS OF WISDOM

BONUS 1: SURVIVAL HERB GARDENING - *Inside Out*

BONUS 2: HOW TO BUILD A WICKING BED SYSTEM -
Another water conserving gardening technique

BONUS 3: HOOP HOUSE MAGIC - *An inexpensive flexible
structure*

Introduction

You are what you eat.

This slogan comes at you from so many sources, to the point that you've almost stopped hearing it.

But the fact is, it's true. When you go to your supermarket, don't you expect to find fresh, clean fruits and vegetables? It is natural for us to be drawn to bright colors and crisp textures.

Consider that today our fruits and vegetables come from all around the world and those countries may not have in place the same farming standards. On the one hand, we have access to foods that are not grown in America, but on the other hand, we have to use caution when buying these crops because they are grown with little or no attention paid to food safety.

Also, the foods we are buying have been shipped over thousands of miles, handled by who knows how many, before they reach our supermarkets. I hate to think what could have happened between the farms and our communities.

With the cost of gas ever increasing and inflation on the rise, it is becoming more expensive to feed our families. Last growing season, all over the globe, farmers experienced poor growing seasons; frosts ruining citrus orchards, tornadoes obliterating farms, droughts causing crops to wither and blow away.

SO WHAT DO WE DO?

I am here to provide your answer, a solution that will blow your mind. Imagine being able to grow your own vegetables and raise your own fresh water fish simultaneously!!! And in your own garden. This probably sounds impossible, but it is very true. This is done by a process known as Aquaponics.

I am going to show you, step by step, how you can successfully set up your own Aquaponics system. To be honest, there is some work involved if you want to be successful, but the benefits more than outweigh your labor.

THE GREAT BENEFITS OF AQUAPONICS:

1. **Taking control of your food supply!** You remove any worries you may have about the freshness or quality of the fruits and vegetables you will serve to your family.

2. **A sustainable system.** Aquaponics mimics nature and by using this method of home farming, there is no negative effect on the environment.

3. **Easy Work.** Unlike conventional gardening, you will not need a large space. No digging or weeding and no bending. Another benefit is that everyone can build and do required maintenance, regardless of physical abilities.

4. **Indoors or Outdoors.** That's just it –you make the choice. The system works just as well in either location.

5. **Simple Operation.** You feed the fish, propagate the seeds and harvest your food.

6. **Count Your Savings.** The system is more productive and efficient than conventional gardens and easy to build economically. It will pay for itself in less than 12 months.

7. **Upgrading.** You can always upgrade to a bigger system or even grow more than your family needs and start your own small business.

I. WHAT IS AQUAPONICS?

Aquaponics is the combination of aquaculture (fish farming) and hydroponics (soil-less plant culture). In Aquaponics, the nutrient-rich water resulting from raising fish provides a natural fertilizer for the growing plants. As the plants consume the nutrients, they help to purify the water in which the fish live. A natural microbial process keeps both the fish and plants healthy, and helps sustain an environment where all can thrive. Essentially, Aquaponics is organic gardening, without the soil.

In Aquaponics, both fish and plants are grown in one body of water, using one "infrastructure". Water circulates from the fish tank, through a biofilter/clarifier if present, to the plant grow beds and then flows back to the fish tanks, completing the loop. Other than an occasional supplement, the use of fertilizer is not required because the fish waste provides the nutrients the plants need. The daily water use is minimal, and a large volume of food crops can be grown using much less space compared to growing crops in a conventional garden. Since soil isn't required, Aquaponics can be set up in urban areas supplying food to local markets, in arid regions with poor soil, in developing countries, in rural communities, in a small backyard, or in an apartment; anywhere that fresh food is needed. Aquaponics is one of the most sustainable and productive farming systems in the world.

Consider the Following:

- Aquaponics uses 90% less water than a conventional garden.

- Aquaponics uses a tiny amount of energy, less than a light bulb.

- Aquaponics can produce up to ten times more vegetables in the same area and time as a garden.

- Labor required to produce plentiful crops is reduced as much as 40%.

HOW MUCH FOOD CAN I GROW WITH AN AQUAPONIC SYSTEM?

The number of plants you can grow is directly proportional to:

1. The number of fish

2. The size of the fish

3. The type of fish

4. The amount of fish added or removed

5. The amount of food being fed to the fish

6. The type of food being fed the fish

7. The types of plants you are growing

8. The time of the year

9. The geographical location of your system

10. The current cycle level of your system

There are many factors involved in the amount of food production your system will support. Each of these is covered in the following chapters. Generally, under reasonable conditions, every pound of fish can produce 70 pounds of fruit and vegetables.

HOW DIFFICULT IS IT TO BUILD AN AQUAPONIC SYSTEM?

Quite simple. A basic Aquaponic system consists of a fish tank, a plant trough, an aquarium pump, a water pump, and a few peripheral items such as tubing, air stones, a thermometer, and testing items. That's it.

Once you have everything together, your fully functioning system can be operating within about a half hour. This does not include the cycling of your system, but if your water is chlorine free, you are ready to get going with the fish and plants.

HOW DIFFICULT IS IT TO OPERATE AN AQUAPONIC SYSTEM?

Since an Aquaponic system is composed of three distinctly different ecosystems, wide temperature fluctuations can greatly impact the health of your system and food production. Once your Aquaponic system is up and cycled, nature takes over and there is very little to do.

Unlike conventional gardening, there is no:

- Weeding
- Fertilizing
- Tilling
- Plowing
- Cultivating
- Composting
- Irrigating
- Spraying for soil pests

Once an Aquaponic system is fully cycled, there is very little to do. Nature takes over and only minor periodic maintenance is required. No more backbreaking work! This will free your time up to do all the chores listed above in your conventional garden.

CAN I FEED MY FAMILY WITH JUST AQUAPONICS?

Yes, but the real question is: "do I want all my eggs in one basket?" The lesson we must learn from our ancestors is that backup systems and redundancy are crucial to survival. An Aquaponic system, like a traditional garden, is susceptible to the same natural threats that can compromise any personal food production system. It is

advisable to consider having other food production resources available such as a conventional gardens, fruit trees, chickens, rabbits, etc. if possible.

II. THE SCIENCE OF AQUAPONICS

THE NITROGEN CYCLE

Ammonia, nitrites, and nitrates are all forms of nitrogen that exist within any Aquaponics system. Beneficial bacteria within an Aquaponics system convert ammonia into nitrites and then into nitrates. Nitrates are then utilized by the plants and flourish within the system. One of the most important yet least understood aspects of Aquaponics is the bacteria. Since they are not visible to the naked eye, they tend to be ignored. But they are essential to the Nitrogen Cycle, which is what makes Aquaponics work.

The Actual Nitrifying Cycle is simple:

1. Fish excrete ammonia (waste),

2. The ammonia is converted ultimately to nitrates by the bacteria,

3. Plants absorb the nitrates and clean the water,

4. Clean water is cycled back into the fish tank.

It's that simple, but each stage is crucial to understand. Let's look at this in more detail.

THE FISH

Fish excrete ammonia, which is toxic to them. In large bodies of water, that is not a problem because of dilution. But in an enclosed tank, this accumulates quickly and becomes deadly.  Excess ammonia can cause tissue damage to fish's gills and kidneys, impair their resistance to diseases, and stunt growth. In an Aquaponic system, ammonia is also toxic to the bacteria and plants. The only practical way to reduce a sudden "spike" in ammonia is to do a partial water change.

You must never overfeed the fish as this will also result in the production of more ammonia. Many people choose to use inexpensive goldfish for the cycling process, due to the minimal cost and their high tolerance to poor water conditions. The best advice you can take when cycling your system is to be patient and let nature take its course.

Do daily water tests during this period and perform water changes as required.

THE BACTERIA

Bacteria break down the ammonia into nutrients on which plants thrive. This is fundamentally a two-stage process. In the first stage, bacteria converts the ammonia into nitrites and is called Nitrosomonas. Nitrites are toxic to fish and interfere with their ability to uptake oxygen. If enough is present in the water, it will kill the fish and bacteria, as well as the plants. Fortunately, a second bacteria comes along called Nitrobacter. It is a slower growing bacteria that feeds on the nitrites. Their waste product is nitrates, which plants love. It is rich in nitrogen, and a great fertilizer. Fish can tolerate a much higher level of nitrates than of ammonia or nitrites.

Things to Know About Nitrifying Bacteria

Nitrosomonas and Nitrobacter are extremely sensitive to sunlight. The water in your fish tank and plant trough must be protected from direct sunlight. There are several species of Nitrosomonas and Nitrobacter bacteria and many strains within those species. In general, the vast majority of this information can be applied to species of Nitrosomonas and Nitrobacter, although, each strain may have different environment and nutrient preferences.

Bacteria colonize all surfaces including rafts, fish, media (gravel or expanded clay), fish tank, and bio-filter. Therefore, the more surface area you can create (such as with a bio-filter), the better for the Nitrogen Cycle.

Nitrifying bacteria have long reproduction times. Under perfect conditions, Nitrosomonas may double every 7 hours and Nitrobacter every 13 hours. Under most conditions, they will double every 15 – 20 hours; this is slow. For reference, in the time it takes for a single Nitrosomonas cell to double in population, a single E. coli bacterium would have produced a population exceeding 35 trillion cells. The upside to them growing slower is that they also die slower and are pretty hearty. There must be plenty of oxygen in the water for nitrifying bacteria to flourish. Also, they cannot survive in dry conditions or handle sustained temperatures higher than 120° F. Of course by that time, you are cooking fish. As a general rule, an uncycled system will require about 4 weeks to cycle completely at around 70° F. It will take longer in colder temperatures.

THE PLANTS

Plants absorb the converted ammonia and flourish. The plants not only clean up the nitrates, they also filter and clean the water as nature intended. Plants can be added at any time during the cycling process, but is not recommended during a "nitrite spike".

THE WATER

Aquaponic water is circulated repeatedly throughout the system. Once it has passed through the plants for cleansing, it is returned to the fish tank to be "re-fertigated". This re-circulation occurs repeatedly and water is generally only added to compensate for evaporation and respiration.

CYCLING AN AQUAPONIC SYSTEM

Cycling an Aquaponic system refers to the point at which the biological process begins in your new Aquaponic System. There are several methods of cycling an Aquaponic system, but there are a few things to keep in mind regardless of which method you apply. Use inexpensive fish. It is recommended you cycle your system using goldfish, which can be purchased at most pet stores. Goldfish (feeder fish) are desirable for several reasons; they are tough little guys, they produce a large amount of ammonia (which is why you seldom see them in an aquarium), and as mentioned, they're not expensive.

Notes on Cycling An Aquaponic System

Keep a Log

It is important to keep a log during this stage of the cycling process which includes dates, times, test reading levels, and record any changes you made to your system. This includes adding or removing fish, plant growth, test results, temperature, and amount of feed, so you can trace issues later. The more detail that is recorded in your log, the more your chances for success or helping others diagnose any system problems for you.

Nitrite Spikes

"Nitrite Spikes" are common during this period. This is when your system is producing more toxic ammonia and nitrites, than the bacteria can break down into harmless nitrates. Refer to Managing a Nitrite Spike for more information on how to deal with this common situation.

Biofilters

Biofilters can help accelerate cycling if you do not have sufficient surface area to populate the nitrifying bacteria. This is usually the case with a raft or NFT system. If you are using a media based system, the media will serve as the Biofilter.

Adding Plants

Plants can be added at any time. You will not realize any significant growth until the cycle is completed and nutrient rich water is being circulated. Think of it as putting a plant in a glass of water, which only keeps it alive. Do not add flowering plants, such fruits such as tomato, cucumber, bell peppers, etc., at this stage as they require way more nutrients than vegetables and will impact all plant growth at this stage.

There are various methods of cycling an Aquaponic system and the most popular are outlined below.

Off-Gassing Chlorine
Chlorine must be off-gassed by letting it sit for a few days in a 5 gallon or so bucket or by bubbling it with an aerator over night. If you are off-gassing a 300-gallon tank or any increment of this volume, bubble the water for 3-5 days then, then always test for chlorine.

CYCLING WITH AMMONIA (FISHLESS CYCLING)

To get your Aquaponic system cycled using ammonia, you must first ensure there is no chlorine in the water. Be sure to sufficiently off-gas the water beforehand. You can start your system's biological process by using ordinary pure ammonia (be sure to check the ingredients). Add 1 teaspoon of pure ammonia a couple of times a week to build up your bacteria colonies. **DO NOT** add too much at a time, as it will then become toxic to the bacteria. Mix ammonia in a bucket first, then slowly add to system. Check your water regularly (every day or two) to ensure the ammonia level does not exceed 1.0 ppm.

Note that when cycling your system, only use pure ammonia, or ammonia with ammonium hydroxide. Any other ingredients will destroy your system. Ammonia bottles labeled as CLEAR AMMONIA may contain surfactants, which will foam if you shake the bottle. It will also kill your fish and bacteria. Perfumes and dyes (such as in bottles of Parson's Ammonia) will kill your fish as well. Sometimes the ingredient list is difficult to find and is mixed in with the directions.

*Always mix ammonia with water
before adding to the plant trough!*

Soon you will realize readings for nitrites, which indicate the first nitrifying bacteria has started processing the ammonia into nitrites.

NOTE: This is the prime time for a Nitrite Spike. Be very cautious at this stage. Don't add any fish until the nitrite level drops back down to zero. Stop adding ammonia at least three days before adding fish. Test the levels and watch for nitrates, which indicate the second nitrifying bacteria have begun to process the nitrites.

CYCLING WITH FISH

To get your Aquaponic system cycled using fish, you must first ensure there is no chlorine in the water. Be sure to sufficiently off-gas the water beforehand. Know that the number of fish you use to cycle your system should be much less than your system is intended to hold. If you use too many fish, there is a danger of a quicker ammonia and nitrite spike, which can compromise the system. This, in turn, will likely kill or severely damage the fish and will require more frequent and larger water changes.

Also, be sure not to overfeed the fish as this will also result in the production of more ammonia. Many people choose to use cheap goldfish for the cycling process, due to the minimal cost and their high tolerance to poor water conditions. The best advice you can take when cycling your system is to be patient and let nature take its course. Do frequent tests (at least daily) during

this period and perform water changes as required. Fish produce ammonia as waste. Depending upon the size of your fish tank, add about 1 goldfish per every 10 gallons. When first introducing the fish into the system, do not feed them for a couple of days until they have had time to acclimate. Check the water quality at least once a week for each week you have been using this method. You will be concerned about ammonia, nitrites, and pH. You will realize the very beginning of full cycling when nitrates appear. Allow the system to operate in this way for two to three weeks until your ammonia and nitrite levels are back very close to zero. If you haven't already, you may add plants at this point.

CYCLING USING ANOTHER AQUAPONIC SYSTEM

To get your Aquaponic system cycled using another Aquaponic system, you must first ensure there is no chlorine in the water. Be sure and sufficiently off-gas the water beforehand. If fish are already present in the system, they will produce ammonia, which will also accelerate the process. Adding a gallon or so of cycled water to your system is the quickest method to get cycled from zero.

The bottom line is, the more previously cycled water you can introduce to your system, the faster it will cycle. This is because you are introducing both nitrifying bacteria and ammonia to your system, which jump-starts the cycling process. You can add previously cycled water at any stage (except during a nitrite spike) of any of the cycling methods described.

Make certain you are getting your cycled water from a source you trust. **DO NOT** use water from a pet store.

Because they routinely deal thousands of fish from all over the world fish diseases are common. They must add a plethora of chemicals to combat this problem. Additionally, these chemicals will be introduced into your systems food chain.

CYCLING WITH PURCHASED NITRIFYING BACTERIA

Nitrifying bacteria is available for purchase from a number of locations. Online, AqauticEco.com carries a product called Nitrifying Bacteria by Proline® which you can add to your water to jump-start the nitrification process. Different quantities can be purchased depending upon your needs. Be sure and sufficiently off-gas the water beforehand. As with pre-cycled Aquaponic water, fish and plants can be added at any time.

Managing a Nitrite Spike

Once your system has sufficient number of nitrifying bacteria to convert the ammonia to nitrates, your system is said to be cycled. At first, there will be more ammonia than bacteria. Then, as the first bacteria starts reproducing there will be more nitrites. This is probably the most critical stage of your Aquaponic system's development. At this point there occurs what is called a "Nitrite Spike". This stage is tough on everything. Testing is critical at this time. Look for indications of stress. Some signs that there is a problem may be that the bubbles are lingering atop the water longer than normal. The water may appear thick and slow moving. The fish may be trying to jump out of the tank, gasping for air (Piping), swimming listlessly, or dying.

At this stage, the best way to level things out is to do a partial water change, that is, replace about 1/3 of the system water with clean, de-chlorinated water. Always have at least this amount of water on hand. When in a nitrite spike, there is no time to off-gas (de-chlorinate) the water. Test the water regularly for indications of nitrates, which are essential to cycling the water.

III. SYSTEM COMPONENTS

At its simplest, an Aquaponic system needs only a fish tank, plant trough, an air and water pump, and a few inexpensive peripherals. While you are free to make the system as complex as you wish, these are the basic parts needed to get you producing abundant food for you and your family.

FISH TANK

The fish tank is where your fish live. They power the system. It is important that they are comfortable, not packed too tightly, not mixed with incompatible fish, and generally not stressed.

There should always be at least two feet of water above them at any time, including when the plant troughs are full of water.

A reasonable amount of water for your fish should be about 5 gallons of water per each pound of fish. This is a full-grown weight. A full-grown Tilapia or Catfish might be about a pound or pound and a half. The fish in your system will be smaller, and if done correctly, staggered for different harvest times. Therefore, many more fish may be added. Just keep in mind this rule of thumb: Do not "overcrowd" your fish.

Types of Tanks

Just about any inert, non-reactive type tank can be used to house your fish. One thing to keep in mind is what the tank is made of. There are many rubber "stock tank" type vessels which work fine. They can be found at feed stores, hardware stores, or hydroponic establishments. The main concern here making sure it is food grade. Most will be.

Fiberglass tanks are acceptable as well as a steel tank with a food-grade vinyl liner. It is not recommended you use a shallow kiddie pool as it is a bit flimsy, does not give the fish the minimum needed two feet of water overhead, and are not considered food grade plastic. Never use an unlined galvanized metal stock tank. As part of the manufacturing process, they are coated in zinc, which will damage fish gills. Also, they do not insulate very well and are susceptible to environmental temperature fluctuations.

Volume Considerations

The size of your fish tank should be determined by the amount of food you wish to produce and is in direct proportion to your plant trough size. As a general rule, a 300-gallon tank will support 2 - 8' x 4' plant troughs, that is, 64 sq. ft.

Therefore, a 150-gallon tank will support 1- 8' x 4' plant trough, that is, 32 sq. ft. This is all very negotiable, as waste produced by your fish will be determined by many factors including fish type, temperature, feeding schedule, time of year and stress.

Environmental Requirements

Because of the potential for intense heat in the summer and the bacteria's susceptibility to direct sunlight, the fish tank must always be covered or shaded! Nitrifying bacteria are very light sensitive and will be killed or greatly inhibited by direct sunlight. A greenhouse would be ideal, but a heavy or solid shade cloth at a minimum is required. Fish do not like to be in the sun and an unprotected tank will heat up quickly. To protect from some of the intense cold snaps, it may be desirable to place carpet or some other insulation under the tank before filling it up to help protect the temperature during the winter. Consider possibly wrapping the outside of the tank in the winter to insulate from the cold. In this case, don't place the tank too close to a wall you cannot get around. In either case, it is a good idea to have a solid cover (or netting if shaded) over the tank when fish are first introduced to the system as many species will attempt to jump out of their new environment.

PLANT TROUGH

Your plant troughs (grow beds) should be thought through before building your system. The size of your beds should  be proportionate to the amount of fish (and feeding) in the system. There are many layout possibilities, but the best one is the one that provides the desired outcome. One consideration is that, depending upon the size of your system, each grow bed has the same quantity of plants growing in them. This ensures that each trough can process the same amount of fish waste.

Plant Trough Size Considerations

Generally, a 300-gallon fish tank can support two 32 sq. ft. plant troughs, that is two 8' x 4' beds. This of course means a 150-gallon tank can support one 32 sq. ft. trough. Support means that there is a proportionate amount of fish in the fish tanks and they are being fed at a rate that supports the number and type of plant you are growing. Also, you will need to install fill & drain and overflow fittings onto the plant trough.

AQUAPONIC SYSTEM PERIPHERALS

There are two pumps used with an Aquaponic system. An air pump and a water pump. The air pump delivers oxygen to the fish through the water, and the water pump circulates the water throughout the system.

Air Pump

A basic two-port aquarium air pump is sufficient to deliver enough oxygen to the fish in a 150-gallon tank. If using a 300-gallon tank, you can use tubing "tees" which allow you to split the hose into two sections, thus giving you four air outlets instead of two. The oxygen value delivered is known as Dissolved Oxygen (DO). This is an imperative component of a healthy system. Be sure and run your air line tubes (with attached air stones) to the bottom of the tank. This increases the surface area of the bubbles bubbling up through the water. If they are at the top of the water column, their functionality is minimized. While too much air bubbling will stress out the fish, be aware that warm water holds less oxygen than cool. It is best to err on the side of caution and over scope the air availability than under estimate.

The air pump must always remain on!

Air Stones

Aeration is critical to raising healthy fish, bacteria, and plants. Air stones help add oxygen to the water by creating an abundant cascade of small bubbles rather than a limited number of larger bubbles from an air tube, thus increasing the surface area. Additionally, they help distribute the oxygen evenly through the water, while aiding in maintaining even water temperature throughout the fish tank. They come in a wide array of varieties and are a matter of preference. Just be sure that they are at the bottom of your tank to maximize their effectiveness.

Water Pump

A water pump circulates the nutrient-rich water into the plant troughs. Most hydroponic plant troughs have two pre-defined spots that can be drilled out for the fill & drain and overflow fittings. The result is that one line is used to pump the water into the plant trough; the other is used as definable overflow drain. That is, the water pumps up to a pre-defined level then drains back into the fish tank via the overflow fitting. This prevents water from pouring over the sides of the plant trough.

With an ebb and flow system, once the water pump turns off, the water backflows through the water pump back into the tank. With a constant flow system, the water pump never turns off. That being said, it is important that you size your water pump correctly. If it is too big a pump, it will overwhelm your threshold and flow over the sides of your plant trough. If it is too small, it will not sufficiently fill the trough in the allotted time. Pump size will be determined by the size of your fish tank and plant trough(s).

Another consideration is the contact time the plant roots have with the water. With an ebb and flow system, you want to ensure adequate time for your plant roots to absorb nutrients and that the water does not flow out of the trough too rapidly. A properly sized Overflow Fitting will ensure enough contact time.

Tubing

Tubing is used to distribute air and water throughout the system; 1/4" tubing is used for air, and 1"–2" is used for water. It is always good to use more than required in case you need to move the system around. Dark tubing is desirable for the water tubes due to algae growth and bacteria sensitivity. Tubing color does not matter for the air lines.

Timers

Timers are used with ebb and flow systems to time water cycles. They regulate when the water pump comes on and turns off, and the duration. They are inexpensive and reliable. They are not needed with a constant flow system as the water pump stays on constantly. The water pump is connected directly to the timer, which is plugged into an electric socket. Generally for Aquaponic applications, the timer is set to turn the water pump on for 15 minutes per hour. This fills the plant trough, hits the threshold level, and then cuts off. Since the water backflows slower through the water pump, there is a lag time and the plant roots are exposed the nutrient-rich water for about 1/2 an hour, each hour, which is desirable. This is known as contact time and critical to growing abundant plants. In other words, plant roots can only absorb nutrients so fast, and therefore need a specific amount of contact time with the water that carries the nutrients.

Autosiphons with an Ebb and Flow System

Autosiphons are often used in place of a timer, which turns the water pump on and off at set intervals. An autosiphon allows the water pump to run constantly, while regulating the ebb and flow cycle. Bell siphons are the most popular. Others include J-bend, loop siphon, and pivot siphon.

A basic bell siphon consists of a vertical standpipe for water to drain into from the plant trough and out to the fish tank. Surrounding the standpipe is another larger, open-ended pipe, called the siphon pipe, with strategically sized holes for water flow. The holes should be big enough for water to flow through, but not the media in the bed to get through. It is important that the pipes are straight. An airtight cap on top of the inner pipe allows the creation of a water vortex. Once the water reaches the top of the inner standpipe, the vacuum is broken and the water is released back into the fish tank.

When using a bell siphon, the maximum height of water in the siphon should match the maximum height of water in the plant trough. Therefore, you may need to adjust the siphon height. It is important to note, this is a mechanical component and can be prone to malfunction.

Thermometer

A thermometer is important as both your fish and bacteria have specific temperature ranges they can tolerate. During hot and cold times, they are both affected by water temperature. Additionally, depending upon your fish species, temperature will determine how much you will feed them. A thermometer is a must-have.

Test Equipment

Testing your system is imperative, especially during the cycling phase. Water testing equipment generally comes in three forms – test strips, reagents (liquids), and electronic equipment. Test strips have various test pads on the strip and, when dipped in the water, change color according to outcome of the test. Reagents are liquids that are mixed with the tank water. Sometimes two different solutions are used and the test results are determined by the water's color after mixing. Electronic testing equipment can get expensive and is limited to only a few tests involving Aquaponics. Some available tests are pH, Dissolved Oxygen, and Temperature.

Nets

Various sized nets are desirable. Larger nets help in catching larger fish as well as small, but it is nice to have a very fine mesh net for cleaning out the fish tank. Fish waste, uneaten food, leaves, dead fish etc. are much easier to collect with this type of net.

Biofilter (Biological Filtration)

Biofiltration is a biological process that helps an Aquaponic system convert toxic wastes (ammonia and nitrites) to non-toxic nitrates. A biofilter is a component that is designed to create surface area on which nitrifying bacteria can grow (colonize).

They can be made from many different materials such as gravel, shell, plastic beads, mesh, hair curlers, or fiberglass matting. What is important is that none of the materials are toxic, and that they will not react with the water nor dissolve or rot over time. Many times a biofilter is nothing more than a container which contains these materials that the water flows through from the fish tank. A biofilter is usually located between the fish tank and the plant trough. Biofilters are often used in conjunction with a clarifier and situated after clarification.

Clarifier (Solid Filters/Mechanical Filters)

Mechanical filtration is the removal of solid waste. A type of mechanical filter commonly used in Aquaponics is called a clarifier and most often added to a raft or NFT system. It is generally located between the fish tank and plant trough and before the biofilter. The principle is simple; as water flows from the fish tank to the plant trough, heavy particles of solid waste fall to the bottom of the clarifier and can be easily collected. Smaller particulate matter is preserved (suspended) and remains in the water to be trapped by the biofilter and converted to essential elements and trace minerals for the plants.

IV. SCOPING YOUR SYSTEM

HOW THIS IS DONE

There are many formulas that can help optimize your food production. Some are based on the amount of food you feed your fish, the size of your grow trough, and plant ratios. Many of these formulas were created on an academic level, i.e. research and development, or on a commercial level where absolute maximum yields must be realized for profit. For personal food production, this does not need to be so complicated. System sizes and ratios are easy to understand and thus become profitable in terms of food production.

SYSTEM SIZING

Scoping an Aquaponic system is not an exact science. There are limitless configuration possibilities, and many conditions can exist that will create variations. For example, the size and type of fish you are stocking, temperature fluctuations, cycle stage of your water, and the time of year will affect production. There are varying results, differing research, and many approaches. Below are some general guidelines based on a 150-gallon fish tank with an 8 x 4 plant trough. As a general rule, simply multiply the ratios for larger or smaller tanks and troughs.

General System Setup Guidelines for a 150 Gallon Aquaponic System:

Tank Volume...150 gallons

Pounds of Fish in Tank............30 +* *(depending on size and conditions)*

Fish Tank Depth... 24" of water

Plant Trough Area...32 Sq. Ft.

Plant Trough Depth................................. 6 inches *(purchased)*

Plant Trough Volume...16 cf

Plant Trough Capacity.................. 120 gallons* *(raft system)*

Plant Trough Water Weight *(raft)*...........................1000 lbs.*

Water Pump flow rate *(GPH/GPM)* 185/3.08

Air Pump Type ....Dual-port Aquarium Pump

Approximate values. View the Aquaponic Boundaries for more details. Remember, larger systems can adapt and absorb changes easier than a smaller system. In other words, a larger system is more forgiving, although if things go south, they do it in a big way. Expand slowly.

WHICH FISH ARE BEST FOR AQUAPONICS?

There is a wide variety of fish available for Aquaponics. They all produce the same kind of waste. The thing to keep in mind is that some fish are not compatible with other fish. For example, Tilapia are Cichlids and don't play well with others. The size of the fish is another consideration. Make sure your fish breeds are all relatively the same size as smaller fish may start to look tasty to some of the larger fish. Be aware that some fish, such as largemouth bass, are carnivorous and will require live food at some point in their growth.

Following is a Partial List of Acceptable Fish for Aquaponics:

- Angelfish
- Barramundi
- Carp
- Golden perch
- Guppies
- Jade perch
- Mollies
- Pacu
- Silver perch
- Sunfish
- Tetras
- Yellow perch
- Channel catfish
- Coppernose blue gill
- Crappie
- Goldfish/Koi
- Hybrid blue gill
- Largemouth bass
- Red ear sunfish

- Tilapia

- Triploid carp

PLANT CONSIDERATIONS

When an Aquaponic system is first being cycled, nutrients are minimal and will not support a fully stocked system. Therefore, if you are using two plant troughs and one can be isolated (turned off), the circulating water can then be focused on one trough.

 At this time you will want to plant green, leafy crops such as lettuce, basil, spinach and herbs. Fruiting plants, such as tomatoes, cucumbers and melons, require much higher nutrient levels than green leafy crops, and if planted too soon will absorb most of the few nutrients available, thus depleting both the greens and themselves of nutrition; in essence, nothing will prosper.

NOTE: **DO NOT** plant mint in your Aquaponic system. The roots will take over everything!

Start with Green, Leafy Crops

- Arugula

- Basil

- Cauliflower

- Chives

- Cabbage

- Head Lettuce
- Leafy lettuce
- Kale
- Mustard Greens
- Pak & Bok choi
- Parsnip
- Parsley
- Radish
- Shallot
- Spinach
- Swiss chard
- Leeks
- Broccoli
- Greens
- Cilantro

Fruiting crops: *(require more nutrients)*

- Beans
- Cantaloupe
- Cucumbers
- Peas
- Peppers
- Squash
- Okra

- Tomatoes

- Watermelon

- Bell Peppers

- Strawberries

- Eggplant

The Best Plants for Aquaponics

We are still learning which plants grow well in Aquaponics. There seems to be an endless list, but those listed above are some that have been tested and do well, depending upon your specific region.

There are many considerations when choosing your plants such as proper season, lighting, temperature, pH, compatibility, and nutrient requirements. Outside of a greenhouse, planting and harvesting cycles in Aquaponics are generally the same for conventional regional crops. If possible, be sure and plant taller plants to the north and your shorter ones to the south to minimize shade issues.

ENVIRONMENTAL CONSIDERATIONS

The best of all worlds is to house your Aquaponic system in a greenhouse. Not everyone has this luxury, but there are many ways outside of a greenhouse to prosper with Aquaponics. Paramount to your success in Aquaponics is the location of your system. There are several considerations to take into account and must all be considered in order to maximize your food yield and protect your system.

Sun Path

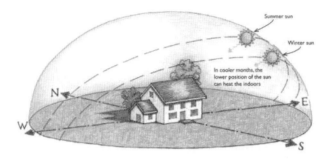

In choosing a location for your system, keep in mind that the plants require sunlight, but the fish do not. Your fish tank should be protected from direct sunlight at all times. Direct sunlight will kill your nitrifying bacteria, deplete oxygen levels in the water, stress out the fish, and cause unwanted heating during warm months.

If possible, orient your grow bed north and south. This will allow for best sun exposure and air circulation. If the rows run east and west plants tend to shade each other. To guard against shade, tall crops such as peas and beans should be planted on the north side of the plant trough. Medium sized crops such as cabbage, cauliflower, broccoli, tomatoes, squash, should be arranged in the center of the trough. At the very southern end of the trough, low growing crops such as radishes lettuce, and chives should be planted.

Trees and Foliage

Avoid placing your system under trees or near bushes and shrubs. They tend to block critical sunlight and will pollute your system when it rains. Falling leaves and small twigs will find their way into the system and decompose thus raising the ammonia level if not outright clogging it up. Some trees, such as pecan, produce a chemical that will kill the fish. Do not set up your system near a pecan tree!

Wind Considerations

A primary concern is wind. If you can place your system close to a fence or building (keeping rain runoff in mind), then this would be ideal. This can serve two purposes: first as a wind block, and second as a structure on which to attach a plastic hoop house for your fish if you wish. During cold weather, this will make a very big difference to the health of your system.

Be sure everything with regard to your system is firmly attached. Make sure the fish tank cover is secure to protect the fish from sun and flying debris. Your shade cloth should be attached securely and designed in such a way that should it come undone, it will not brutalize your plants during a windstorm.

Slope

To ensure even distribution of nutrients, it is very important to place your system on level ground. A constant flow system requires that water flow freely without producing "eddies", that is, areas where water is not exchanged and thus becomes void of nutrients (dead zones). Make certain the ground is solid to avoid settling under the weight of the system. Rain can soften the ground and cause uneven settling which will be difficult to correct after the system is built and operating.

Seasonal Issues

Always design and construct your Aquaponic system with the various seasons in mind. It is important to be prepared for rapid changes that will affect the fish and plants. Be aware of the temperature issues outlined below, while keeping in mind that the amount of sunlight available is diminished during the winter months.

During the spring there tends to be long periods of rain, which will fill your system to the brim. If you have a media system, this may expose the upper levels of water in the plant trough to direct sunlight, which may compromise your bacteria. Consider a shade cloth or emptying some of the water. The opposite is true in the summer. Evaporation is at its highest during this time and it will become necessary to "top off" the system more often. Be certain to always have de-chlorinated water available.

Temperatures

Because of erratic temperature shifts, certain considerations must be taken into account when placing your Aquaponic system. Protect the fish tank in cold weather by provide a vertical foundation for a plastic hoop house structure. If a hoop structure is not an option, consider putting the system next to a wall to the sun path be used as a structure on which to connect plastic sheeting for protection from the elements. Conversely, it can also provide a source of shade during the hot summer months. It would be wise to attach shade cloth to the plant trough to avoid sun scorching of plants and unnecessary heating of the water.

Cold Temperatures

When setting up the fish tank, it may be desirable to put a carpet remnant underneath it to insulate it from the cold ground in the winter. Additionally, ensure that the tank is far enough away from any obstructions so you can wrap it with insulation should it be required. A styrofoam fish tank cover (can be made from raft material) will also help retain heat. Consider turning the water pump off at night to further conserve heat. Note this is the water pump not the air pump, which should never be turned off. Remove any type of shade cloth that is over the plants as the sunlight will help warm the water during the day.

If you'd like to use a heater in the water, be aware that a livestock tank de-icer will not work. Most of their thermostats kick on at about 40° F, which is way too late for your fish. Water does not need to be a toasty 80° F but should not dip below 50° F. Remember that the entire system metabolism slows down in cold weather, so reduce feeding accordingly. The rate of growth for nitrifying bacteria can decrease by up to 75% at 50° F.

Hot Temperatures

 Sustained hot temperatures can wreak havoc on an Aquaponic system. Warmer water holds less oxygen, essential to fish metabolism. High temperatures also affect bacteria. Different fish have different temperature tolerances, so check with your fish provider for their tolerance ranges.

One way to cool water is to add additional aerators. The bubbling action will dissipate heat and oxygenate the water. If possible, raise the return water from the plant trough above the fish tank to cool it on the way down via splashing. Cover the fish tank with bird netting to allow heat dissipation. Be sure the tank is shaded if using netting. Leave the water running overnight to help cool things down. Another great idea is to drop a couple frozen jugs of water into the tank during the heat of the day, and refreeze overnight.

V. DESIGNING YOUR SYSTEM

MAIN TYPES OF BACKYARD SYSTEMS

By and large, Aquaponic "systems" are determined by how the plants are supported, not the fish tank. The three most common type systems used for personal food production are media bed, deep water raft, and NFT (nutrient film technique).

Media Bed

In a media-based Aquaponic system, the plant trough is filled with a pellet-like solid media such as gravel, granite, lava rocks, pebbles or expanded clay beads. The primary purpose of the media is to support the plants and to provide a growing surface for the nitrifying bacteria. As such, a biofilter is not necessary. A clarifier for solids removal can be placed between the fish tank and plant trough if desired.

Almost any material will suffice but you must make certain the media is inert and will not react with the water. If the media came from an area with a lot of limestone in the ground, it will affect the pH balance. Also be certain the media is well washed before circulating the water from the fish tank.

The primary advantage of a media based system is that the media becomes a bio-filter. This is due to the large amount of surface area created by the media, which gives nitrifying bacteria ample surface area to populate. Additionally, as long as the water is sufficiently aerated, worms can be added to the grow bed thus adding to the nutrient content of the water.

Another advantage is that plants can be easily moved around in the grow bed.

The primary disadvantages are that the media can be very heavy, and tend to absorb heat in the summer and retain cold in the winter. Also, if the system is not in correct balance, waste can build up within the media causing further imbalance. Cleaning can be difficult. Vertical water zones must be observed in the plant trough as any water at the highest levels may be exposed to sunlight, which will kill the nitrifying bacteria. For this reason, the water must stay below the top few inches of media.

Deep-Water Raft

In a raft system, cut-to-size styrofoam sheets (rafts) are used to float in the diffusing water to cool plant troughs. These 4' x 8' insulation sheets can be purchased at any major home improvement store. Various sized holes, usually from 2" – 4" in diameter are cut into the raft. Plants are then placed in small plastic mesh baskets and inserted into the holes. The roots dangle in the water.

The primary advantages of raft systems are that they are easy to maintain, insulate the water during weather extremes, and protect the water from direct  sunlight. Due to the large volume of water involved, the water temperature and pH balance tends to remain more stable than with other methods. Additionally, when the rafts are cut into smaller sections, harvesting can be made easier as one section at time can be lifted out.

The primary disadvantages of a raft system is the lack of surface area for nitrifying bacteria, the absence of worms, and inability to move plants around (plants must remain in pre-defined holes). Additionally, a biofilter and clarifier should be incorporated. These are often added to raft systems in order to increase surface area for the bacteria and to clean out solids. The clarifier removes large solids before water is pumped into the grow bed.

Nutrient Film Technique (NFT)

With a NFT system, long pipes, usually made of PVC, have holes cut in the top to hold plastic mesh baskets. Plants are inserted into the baskets and the roots "dangle" into the pipe. A steady stream of nutrient-rich water (nutrient film) is constantly pumped through the pipe, which waters the roots tips. Proper slope must be carefully observed with this type system. It is very important to filter the water well before sending it into the NFT trough since solid fish waste in the trough and on the plant roots will negatively impact the plant's growth. NFT Aquaponics requires clarification and biofiltration.

While the reduced amount of water needed to fill the system may seem like a benefit, it can mean greater temperature and water quality fluctuations in a short period of time. One of the primary advantages to NFT is that the water constantly flows a media based plant trough mesh basket for plants through the pipes and the bottoms of the dangling roots are exposed to the nutrient-rich water while the upper portion is exposed to the air (oxygen). Another advantage is that a minimal use of space is required since the pipes can be arranged vertically. A relatively small of amount of fish is required due to the minimized amount of water required for this type of system.

The primary disadvantage of NFT is a minimal surface area for bacteria to grow on and only a certain amount of holes can be cut into the pipes for plants. Due to a lack of surface area commonly found in media bed or raft systems, a biofilter and clarifier is always required so that the beneficial bacteria have sufficient surface area to cultivate and solids are removed or broken down. Due to the small volume of water used, NFT systems are extremely susceptible to temperature and pH swings.

OTHER SYSTEM TYPES

There are many other types of Aquaponic systems, such as towers that are trickle-fed from the top, plastic barrels cut in half with gravel or rafts in them, IBC totes (Intermediate Bulk Containers), and living room aquarium setups. Each system has its own advantages and disadvantages, but all operate on the same fundamental principles.

SIMPLE SYSTEM PHYSICS AND WATER FLOW OPTIONS

There are several water delivery options available for backyard Aquaponics, but regardless of the water flow option you choose, they are all based on a water pump that either stays on all the time or is controlled by a timer or other device. The water pump is generally situated either inside or outside the fish tank (as opposed to the plant trough or biofilter/clarifier). If the water pump (submersible) is situated inside the fish tank, it will be pushing the water. If outside the fish tank it will be pulling water. The relevance here is gravity. To conserve energy and wear and tear on your water pump, your fish tank or plant trough should be higher than the other.

FISH TANK HIGHER THAN PLANT TROUGH

If the fish tank is higher than the plant trough, water will flow automatically via gravity through the drain into the trough. It may travel though a biofilter and clarifier, but ultimately the water ends up in the trough. There must be a pump at the end of the line to "pull" the water from the trough and pump it back into the fish tank.

Plant Trough Higher than Fish Tank

If the plant trough is higher than the fish tank, a submersible water pump in the fish tank must "push" the water into the plant trough against gravity. Since the plant trough is higher than the fish tank, once the plant trough fills, gravity takes over and the water flows back into the fish tank.

Note: there need only be a couple of inches difference in heights. Water always finds the easiest route to level.

AQUAPONIC WATER FLOW OPTIONS

Continuous Flow

Continuous flow systems pump water continuously throughout the entire system. Sometimes, it may make some plants susceptible to root rot due to lack of oxygen. For this reason it is important to ensure this type of system is well aerated. Also, it must be ensured there are no eddies forming, that is, dead zones where nutrient-rich water isn't continually exchanged.

One solution to this problem is, using PVC or plastic tubing, to run the water to the other end of the plant trough so it must travel back through to the drain on the opposite side.

Ebb and Flow/Flood and Drain/ Intermittent Flow

This water flow method is designed to pump water to the plant troughs at pre-defined intervals generally either by means of an electric timer attached to the water pump, or via an autosiphon. Using an autosiphon, the water pump runs continuously and floods and drains out of the grow bed once it is filled.

Flood and drain times vary between setups. There is no specific length of fill and drain times. These are determined by the size of your plant trough and pumping capacity of your water pump. A good rule of thumb is 15 minutes per hour. During this amount of time, the plant trough fills with water and when full, drains out the overflow tube back into the fish tank. Once the pump turns off, the water level drops to below the overflow threshold and then continues to drain back slowly through the water pump for about another 15 minutes for a total of  about a half hour. This ensures adequate root contact time with the nutrient-rich water. The water pumps can be turned off at night to conserve heat or electricity.

VI. PULLING IT ALL TOGETHER

We have discussed the Science of Aquaponics, the system components that make up a basic system, how to scope a system and designing a system which included system types and water flow options. Now we will look at putting it all together. In its most basic form, an Aquaponics system is quite simple. There is a fish tank, a plant trough, water and air pump, some tubing and a few ancillary items.

For simplicity, we will construct a store bought system, using the components for the system pictured above. This is a 150-gallon rubber stock tank and a 6' x 3' plant trough. Any variation of this can be used as long as none of the parts affect the water quality and integrity of the system. In other words, everything should be "food grade". The concepts for constructing this system are the same no matter how you design your Aquaponic system.

FILL AND DRAIN, AND OVERFLOW FITTINGS

First thing to do is drill out the water intake and outflow holes in the plant trough (two holes side by side). Most store-bought hydroponic plant troughs have pre-defined hole slots that are usually drilled out at the store. Afterwards, the Fill and Drain, and Overflow fittings must be installed. They simply screw into either hole in the trough. The Fill & Drain fittings generally accept a 1/2" tubing and come with rubber gaskets for a watertight fit.

The overflow fitting can be adjusted by adding extensions to conform to the plant trough height and generally accepts a 3/4" size tubing. When the water fish tank and plant trough pump turns on, the water level rises to the height of the overflow level. Then the water drains back into the fish tank so the plant trough does not overflow. When the water pump turns off, the level drops to below the overflow height and then drains out the Fill and Drain fitting through the water pump.

POSITION AND LEVEL THE FISH TANK AND PLANT TROUGH

Next, ensure that the fish tank and plant trough are level. This is very important. It may be a good idea to place a large piece of carpet under the fish tank to help insulate it during cold temperatures. Also, when you are filling the system with water, check the level periodically and make adjustments as necessary. Using whatever means you desire to support the plant trough, ensure the plant trough hangs over the fish tank enough so that water will drain straight down from the plant trough via either fitting. If not, tubing can be extended to make up the difference in distance between the trough and tank. The advantage to the water splashing straight down from the trough is added oxygenation for the fish.

DRILL HOLES IN THE FISH TANK

It is prudent to distribute as much of the air throughout the fish tank as possible. This is easily  accomplished by drilling two holes on either side of the tank, or four holes equidistant around the perimeter of the tank. Measure amount of tubing needed to reach from the air pump to the air stones. Remember to always locate the stones at the bottom of the fish tank to maximize water contact with the bubbles. Tee fittings can be purchased to split the one hose into two hoses. Next connect the air hoses to air pump. Run the hose through the holes in the tank and connect the air stones.

CONNECT THE WATER PUMP

If your water pump is submersible, connect one end of the 1/2" hose to the Fill & Drain fitting and the other to the water pump. It is desirable to keep the water pump tube as short as practical to avoid disturbing the fish and hindering fish capture. Most pumps come with various size joiners to adapt to your tubing size. Position the water pump in the fish tank, preferably to one side.

FILL THE TANK WITH WATER

Fill the fish tank half full and check the level of the tank to ensure it is even. Make adjustments if necessary, then fill to about two inches below the top. If using municipal water; that is, chlorinated water, turn on the water pump and air pump and leave both pumps running for two days. Check for leaks. Then, check to ensure all chlorine has off-gassed. When the water is completely off-gassed, turn the water pump off.

FILL THE PLANT TROUGH WITH MEDIA OR CUT

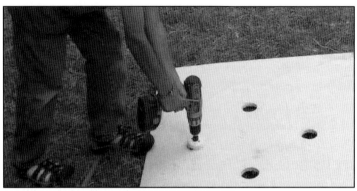

RAFTS TO SUIT YOUR SYSTEM TYPE

If you are using a media based system, be sure and rinse the media off thoroughly before introducing it to your system, especially if it is expanded clay. Small particulate matter will clog things and adversely affect the fish.

If you are using a raft system, cut the size holes you need using a hole saw in the raft. The size holes are determined by your basket size for the plants. Most practical Aquaponic baskets require 3" holes. Make sure all the debris from the drilling is washed off completely.

Sometimes it is desirable to paint the raft white. If you choose to do so, be certain to use a non-toxic latex paint and paint the raft before drilling. Paint only the side that will be facing up. Be sure and  thoroughly rinse the raft off several times, letting it dry between rinsing. When there is no more foam coming off the raft, it is safe to drill and use in the system. Don't drill more holes than you need. Unfilled holes will expose the water to damaging sunlight.

READY THE SYSTEM FOR CYCLING

Check the tubing and ensure they are all snugly attached to their fittings. Look for any leaks throughout the system. Test to ensure that the chlorine has been completely off-gassed. If there is sediment from the media, be sure and clean it out. Now, refer to Cycling a System.

A good trick: If you are testing for chlorine using a multi-test strip, use a neutral object such as a clean piece of plastic strip, and drip a drop of water on only the chlorine pad part of the test strip. They are expensive and once the chlorine is off-gassed, the test is moot. Save the rest of the tests for later.

VII. OPERATING YOUR AQUAPONIC SYSTEM

FEEDING THE FISH

It is critical to never overfeed your fish, especially when things are unstable, regardless of the reason for the instability. This will ultimately produce more ammonia and throw the system into further imbalance. Do not feed more than is consumed within about 2 minutes. Any uneaten fish food should be removed from the tank. Most Aquaponic fish are happy eating regular Catfish food that can be purchased from almost any feed store. Just be certain it contains at least 32% protein. Smaller pellets are desirable to accommodate the smaller fish. Use floating fish food if possible to minimize accumulation on the bottom.

MONITORING THE SYSTEM - SIGHTS, SOUNDS, AND SMELLS

Over time, and by being observant, you will get to know your Aquaponic system. There are three separate ecosystems existing within the system, each with different characteristics and needs. There are several tasks which you should become familiar with, so that they will become automatic every time you approach your system.

Water

The water in your Aquaponic system should always appear clean to the degree that there isn't an excessive amount of solid debris suspended or lingering on the bottom. Air bubbles should appear crisp and pop relatively quickly. If air bubbles linger too long before they "pop", it is an indication of a bacteria problem. See Bacteria in the section below for more information.

Learn to listen to the system. If you walk up to your fish tank and there is no sound of bubbles, something is wrong. You may still hear the air pump, but the tubing may have slipped off the pump. Perhaps the air pump got unplugged but yet you still hear the sound of the water flowing out of your plant trough. When it comes to air, you have very little time before your fish are damaged due to lack of oxygen.

A properly cycled Aquaponic system should never smell bad. In fact, when properly cycled and in balance, it should smell fresh and clean. A bad odor usually means there are dead fish in the system, or there is a bacteria problem. Check the system for obvious problems, then test the water to determine the best course of action.

Fish

Depending upon the type of fish you are raising, they should generally be active and moving about happily. Learn to recognize what they look like in this state. The way you will know something is wrong when they are acting differently - moving sluggishly, listing to one side, swimming upside down. Perhaps you have lost a fish, not a big thing, but if you lose several over a couple of days, this indicates a problem.

If you observe fish swimming towards the top of the tank and gulping for air, this is known as piping. This indicates a definite problem that must be addressed immediately.

This could be a lack of oxygen, a high level of ammonia or nitrites, or a foreign substance that has been introduced into the water. Test the water and determine the best course of action.

Listen for uncharacteristic splashing or thrashing of the water. This may an indication that the fish are trying to escape their environment or stressed. This may be caused by many things such as water imbalance, temperature, a fish disease, or low oxygen. Depending upon the color of your fish tank, it is convenient to have fish that contrast with it so they will be easier to observe. In other words, black fish in a black tank are hard to see and thus monitor and catch.

One of the most common, and highly contagious diseases your fish may encounter is known as "ick" (Ichthyophthirius multifiliis). This presents itself as little white spots on the fish. If you see your fish rubbing themselves rapidly on the bottom or sides of the tank, this is an indication that they may be infected. While there are chemical treatments for ick, it is not wise to use them in an Aquaponic system where the food will be eaten. Aquarium salt can be used, but if you have a very large tank, it will require a lot of salt and it may affect your plants. If possible, isolate the infected fish and treat them independently in warm water.

A bad smell could be a dead fish. Remove it immediately and plant it in your food garden like the pilgrims did.

Bacteria

As mentioned in the Water section above, watching air bubbles can be a good indicator of a bacteria problem. Under normal healthy conditions, air bubbles form quickly, move quickly above the surface of the water, and then pop. When the Aquaponic water appears thick, and bubbles are sluggish and lingering, this is an indication of potential bacteria problem. Imagine a swamp. You may see a difference in your fish's behavior due to increased stress. Outside of an occasional dead fish, any bad odor can usually be attributed to a bacteria problem. Test the water and determine the best course of action.

Plants

Though sounds and smells don't generally relate to plants, they are the most visible. Depending upon what you are growing, your plants should look healthy and vibrant in an Aquaponic system. The primary nutrient deficiencies to keep in mind are Iron, Potassium, and Calcium. A stressed plant may exhibit discoloration (chlorosis), obvious stress, or outright death when the system is out of balance. Fruits may be stagnated or not flourish after flowering. These are all longer term signs of the system being out of balance. Test the water and determine the best course of action.

TESTING

Testing is an integral part of Aquaponics. There are myriad things to consider when it comes to overall system health, and many involve testing of some sort. As mentioned previously, not all testing comes from a test kit. Learn to use your senses first and foremost. In the meantime, you can test for the following which are based on general test kits which may be purchased at any aquarium or pet store.

pH

Because plants prefer a pH of about 6.0 and fish prefer a pH of 8.0, it is common in Aquaponics to compromise and try to keep the system neutral at 7.0. This range satisfies the fish, plants and bacteria. The pH of the system can be raised or lowered depending upon the need. Be certain never to add anything to the system without diluting the substance. That is, dilute the substance in a bucket and add it to the plant trough slowly. When lowering the pH, add the water over the course of the day or so.

NOTE: If you have a media bed and the media contains limestone, it will be extremely difficult to get the pH down. You should get a different media such as granite or expanded clay.

Raising pH

Normal nitrification has a tendency to reduce pH (make more acid). If your Aquaponic water is acidic, this can be kept in check by adding a safe alkaline substance such as calcium carbonate (CaC03). Calcium carbonate increases pH, but stops dissolving at a pH of around 7.4, meaning pH will stay pretty stable until all of the available calcium carbonate is depleted.

Other sources of calcium carbonate include:

- limestone

- shell grit

- seashells

- egg shells

Lowering pH

Aquaponic systems tend to be acidic Hydrochloric or muriatic acid is commonly used to reduce pH levels. Vinegar and lemon juice can also be used in a pinch, but are not as effective as these acids and not recommended. Do not use sulfuric or citric acid. The right quantity of acid to be used is dependent on the buffering capacity of the water. Add a small bit to a five gallon bucket of preferably clean de-chlorinated water, and mix well. Add it slowly to the plant trough. Wait for about a day and check the pH the next day and continue if necessary. pH should always be adjusted slowly.

Some things to know about pH:

The pH scale runs from 0 to 14, with 7 being neutral (neither acid nor alkaline). That is, values below 7 are acid and above are alkaline.

The pH scale is logarithmic. So as the pH moves away from 7, each step up or down is 10 times stronger than the last. In other words, a pH 6 is 10 times and a pH 5 is 100 times more acidic than pH 7. This is why a pH swing of just a couple of units can seriously affect fish and bacteria health and function.

It is important to keep your tank within a healthy range and to avoid major fluctuations within this range over short periods. Fluctuations will stress your fish and could result in death or increased susceptibility to disease. Although the suitable range will vary between species, most freshwater fish can be permanently kept at pH within the range 5.5 to 8.0 and many have a wider range. These ranges of course, are not the same for plants and will affect bacterial processing.

AMMONIA

There are two primary sources of ammonia in an Aquaponic system. The first is excreted by the fish from their gills. The second is produced through natural biological conversion of decaying organic matter (such as uneaten fish food), fish waste, and dead plant matter within the grow-beds (old plant roots). If using a standard ammonia test kit, anything over 2ppm ammonia becomes dangerous to the fish and bacteria. To lower ammonia levels, stop feeding the fish and do a 1/3 water change. That is, pour out a third of the tank and replace with that amount of clean de-chlorinated water. Do this daily until the ammonia drops to a safe level. Begin feeding fish again.

NITRITES

Nitrites affect the ability of the fish's gills to efficiently transfer oxygen to bloodstream. At rates as low as 0.5 ppm, nitrites can be harmful to your fish. This is why managing a nitrite spike during cycling is so critical. This becomes even more significant when oxygen levels in the water are lower, for example from higher temperatures. When cycling your system and the nitrite levels elevate, what is really happening is that your first nitrifying bacteria, Nitrosomonas, is breaking down the ammonia in the water. But, the second nitrifying bacteria, Nitrobacter has not yet populated to significant numbers to process the nitrites into nitrates.

When nitrites are high, stop feeding your fish!

Other factors that may affect elevated nitrite levels are too many fish for your size system, overfeeding, under-developed bacteria for the amount of ammonia being produced, large amounts of decaying matter in the plant troughs, or sunlight hitting the water which kills beneficial bacteria.

To lower nitrite levels, stop feeding the fish and do a 1/3 water change. That is, pour out a third of the tank and replace with that amount of clean de-chlorinated water. Do this daily until the nitrites drop to a safe level. Begin feeding fish again.

NITRATES

Nitrates are not harmful to fish unless in very high quantities. Since it is the plants that absorb the nitrates in an Aquaponic system, there must be an adequate number of plants to balance the production. This is proportional to the system size and number of fish (weight), and feeding ratio.

ALKALINITY AND HARDNESS

Alkalinity and hardness are important in factors in Aquaponics. To a large degree, these two factors regulate the cushion (buffering) power of water to resist pH change. If the water has a higher alkalinity, it is more resistant to pH changes. This is important to the fish, plants and bacteria. To truly understand alkalinity and hardness requires some knowledge of chemistry such as ions, molar concentrations, anions, and buffering, which is beyond the scope of this publication. But following is a high level overview of water alkalinity and hardness as it applies to Aquaponics.

Alkalinity

Alkalinity is the capacity of water to neutralize acids without increasing the pH. In other words, total alkalinity is water's capacity to absorb acids. Thus, water with high alkalinity is able to absorb more acid. The basic ions include bicarbonate (HCO_3), carbonate (CO_{32}), and hydroxide (OH). In Aquaponics, moderate levels of bicarbonate, and carbonate ions are beneficial for fish. Alkalinity is important in Aquaponics to offset the normal buildup of carbon dioxide, which is a source for acid formation. These formations come from normal respiration and bacterial processes which can cause the pH to drop rapidly.

Specifically, if the water is sufficiently alkaline, excess acid is converted by the carbonate ions and the pH remains stable. This is why it is important to choose your media wisely, if a media bed is what you have. You must take this into account with your water source. A neutral media such as expanded clay beads or river rock will have no effect on the pH. Limestone rocks or some other like material will tend to raise the alkalinity level of the water way beyond neutral.

Hardness

Water hardness is similar to alkalinity but represents a measure of calcium ion ($Ca+2$), magnesium ion ($Mg+2$), and other ions for aluminum, iron, manganese, and/or zinc. Often, hardness is confused with alkalinity due to the fact that both $Ca+2$ and CO_{32} ions tend to occur together in waters from areas with high limestone ground consisting of calcium carbonate ($CaCO_3$). There are two primary types of water hardness: general hardness (GH) and carbonate hardness (KH), also known as alkalinity. There is also another called total hardness, which is a combination of GH and KH. Most test kits test for total hardness, which can be misleading. Both GH and KH are important to know, so it is best to test for hardness values individually.

CHLORINE, CHLORAMINES, AND OFF-GASSING

As outlined in the Cycling section, before adding bacteria or fish to your Aquaponic system, all chlorine must be completely "off-gassed". Chlorine must be off-gassed by letting it sit for a few days or by bubbling it overnight, using an air pump, in a 5 gallon (or so) bucket. If you are off-gassing a 300-gallon tank or any increment of this volume, bubble the water for 3-5 days, then test for chlorine. The longer the chlorinated water bubbles using air stones, the more successful your cycling and water change efforts will be as this process also oxygenates the water.

Unfortunately almost all water municipalities now treat drinking water with chloramines. Chloramines are more stable than chlorine (which is a gas, and thus can be 'off-gassed"). But with chloramines it it different. Basically, chloramines are formed by mixing chlorine with ammonia and adding it to our tap water. Yeah, that's right. Careful what you drink. Obviously, this is very significant also to your Aquaponic system, especially during a nitrite spike. If you are unsure whether your water has been treated with chloramines, test for ammonia after off-gassing the chlorine, or call your local water treatment facility and ask questions.

There are several proposed solutions for chloramines such as Thiosulfate, Food Grade Ascorbic Acid (Vitamin C - 1000 mg/40 gal), Zeolite, campden tablets (available at many homebrew stores), and products such as AmQuel (sodium hydroxymethanesulfonate) that can be purchased at an aquarium store. Passing the water through a carbon filter before adding to the system has been recommended. Results vary depending upon how much Choramine is added to your municipal water supply.

Aquaponic systems have operated successfully with chloramines present, and problems usually present themselves during the hotter summer months.

DISSOLVED OXYGEN (DO)

Of all environmental factors that affect an Aquaponic system, one of the most critical is the dissolved oxygen (DO) level in the water. If DO gets below 3 ppm there is a problem and it must be corrected quickly. Acceptable levels are between 4 and 5 ppm, but 6 and above is stellar. A drop in dissolved oxygen may come from the air pump being disconnected on a hot day, or too many fish in the tank.

Make certain that there are adequate air stones in your fish tank and they go all the way to the bottom of the tank. The longer the time the air bubbles are exposed to the water, the more increase in diffusion. Clean the air stones periodically.

VIII. MAINTAINING YOUR SYSTEM

The more cycled and settled your Aquaponic system becomes, the less maintenance it requires. Nature takes over, but this doesn't mean it is maintenance free. There are several key areas that need to be monitored at all times.

KEEPING THE AQUAPONIC SYSTEM CLEAN

It is very important that you keep your Aquaponic system free of leaves, undigested fish food sediment, excessive fish waste, dead fish, and other gunk. These will not only clog your bio-filter and clarifier, they will decompose and can raise your ammonia level, and thus alter the pH and nitrites. In other words, it can throw the overall system out of balance. Keep the fish tank covered as best as possible. This will help eliminate light and minimize things that may slow down your system, as well as to prevent your fish from jumping out of the tank, which is not uncommon.

DO NOT put lotion on your hands prior to handling your system!

DO NOT wash your hands with soap prior to handling your system!

DO NOT use mosquito repellent on your hands prior to handling your system!

Different size nets can be helpful for different sized items needing to be extracted. A net with a fine mesh will help remove suspended particulate matter which breaks down the quickest, while a larger mesh net is good for retrieving fish. When doing things around your Aquaponic system, consider situations which might affect the water quality by contamination such as mowing the lawn (dust and grass), watering your lawn with sprinklers (chlorine), or working on a construction project that might produce saw dust.

PERIODIC WATER CHANGES

After full cycling and proper system balance, you should never need to do a water change. But this does not mean it may not ever be necessary. Observe the water to ensure that it is crisp, clean (murky is ok), and that the bubbles from the air stones or after returning from the plant trough don't linger too long. When this happens, it is an indication that there is a bacterial problem and must be addressed immediately. Look for obvious signs that might cause this, such as those outlined above in the Keeping the Aquaponic Clean section.

Test the water immediately to determine the best course of action. Excessive ammonia, nitrites, or decaying debris in the system can cause these conditions.

A JUDICIOUS PLANT PRUNING

A judicious plant pruning is a fancy way of saying keep your plants trimmed. Excess leaves and branches, near the bottom of the plant, which are usually non-producing, absorb needed nutrients from the plant and the entire system. Remove dead leaves, as they can easily fall into the water and decay thus producing ammonia and changing the balance of the system. It is a good idea to minimize plants overlapping. Plants shading each other blocks sunlight required for photosynthesis.

ROUTINE SCHEDULES

The following routine schedules assume a fully cycled system. During the cycling process, routines such as daily testing are required. At the point of full cycling everything should operate smoothly and the concerns are different. It is very important to learn how to test your system using only your senses. A healthy Aquaponic system has very distinct sounds, appearances, and smells. It is important to learn how to listen, look, and smell your system and know immediately if there is a problem.

Daily

Depending upon the type of fish you have, learn their eating habits and feed rates. Different fish may need to be fed at different intervals. For example, if you have Tilapia, they have small stomachs and large intestines which means they must be fed several times daily; ad libitum, meaning only what they will eat. A good time frame in this case is what they will eat in about 1 - 2 minutes. Anything in excess of this will tend to decay on the bottom and clog the biofilter. Catfish on the other hand need only be fed once a day, ideally in the evening. Be sure and observe the fish. Check to make sure they look vibrant, healthy, and are moving normally. During temperate weather, take note of water temperature and plant conditions. Look, listen, and smell for anything odd.

Observe the System

- Are the air bubbles on top of the water lingering? If so, there could be a bacteria problem. Test the water immediately to determine the best course of action.

- Is the water flowing properly? If not, there may be a restriction somewhere. Check water hoses, pump filter, and plumbing for problems.

- Is the water level the same? If not, could be a blockage somewhere. Check water hoses, pump filter, plumbing and biofilter for problems.

- Are the fish listless or acting differently? This could be a sign of a systemic problem. Test to determine the best course of action.

Listen to the System

If your system is set up for constant flow, do you hear the water pump operating? If not, check that the water pump is in good working condition or has not been unplugged.

- Do you hear water flowing normally? If not, check water hoses, water pump, and plumbing for problems.

- Does the air pump and bubbles sound the same? If not, check for disconnections or blockages.

- Do you hear the sound of thrashing fish? This is a sign of a systemic problem. Test to determine the best course of action.

Smell the System
- Does it smell different? If so, there could be a bacteria or dead fish problem. Test the water immediately to determine the best course of action. Remove any dead fish. Look around the outside of the tank for fish that went exploring.

Look and Smell the Fish
- Are they robust? If not, they may be stressed. Check for stress causing signs such as low water temperature, high or low pH or excess ammonia and nitrites.

- Are they listless? If so, they may lack oxygen, check air pump, hoses, and air stones to ensure air is flowing freely, especially during hot summer months as warm water holds less oxygen.

- Does it smell fishy? Look for diseased fish or a bacteria problem.

- Are they lying on the bottom not moving? Get your net.

Look at the Plants
- Are they droopy? Could be that the water is not flowing into the plant trough correctly. Inspect the water pump, inlets and outlets, and the clarifier and biofilter for water obstructions. Check the timer to ensure it is working properly.

- Have they fallen out of their baskets when the raft ebbed and flowed? Check that the plants are secure in their baskets.

- Do they look "munched out"? Check for insects or fungal disease.

- Are the plants scorched? Consider putting a shade cloth over the plants.

- Get the net! This will also help reduce the temperature of the water.

Weekly

Factors such as temperature, debris build-up, and pH fluctuations will affect your overall system health. It is a good practice to test your water periodically if something seems fishy. This will give you a good indication of any changes that may be occurring.

- Make sure there is not a buildup of fish waste or uneaten food on the bottom of the fish tank.

- Check for plant debris and excess food waste in the plant trough

- Observe if there is any discoloration on the plants. This is a sign of a nutrient deficiency

- Look for fungus, insect infestations, or any other kinds of stress.

Monthly

- Observe the plants and determine if they might need to be amended with iron, potassium, calcium, or other nutrients.

- It is a good idea to closely check all the components of the Aquaponic system once a month. Many water pumps have built in filters, which serve as great "small" biofilters but can easily clog, restricting flow.

- Check air filters and air stones to ensure they are clean and working properly. Any reduction in the volume of bubbles being produced is an indication of a problem.

- Look for opportunistic algae or insects, which may invade the system.

- Observe the change of season and adjust your system appropriately for summer sun, or winter wind.

Annually

Re-think your entire system. Consider what you have learned and how you can check for leaks or improve on the system. Using this knowledge, consider expanding your system if that's your desire. You have been through all four seasons and adjusted for each. Regardless of how each season turned out, your knowledge increased, as well as your experience as a grower, which can lead to larger yields.

Inspect your air and water pumps. Clean them thoroughly. Remember that the water pump filter is loaded with beneficial bacteria so you only want to remove any solid buildup. **DO NOT USE SOAP!** Check all the hoses and fittings for leaks or excessive wear.

IX. FOOD HARVESTING

FISH

Harvesting fish can be tricky, especially with a round fish tank. Depending upon the depth, color of your fish and tank, size, and number of fish, a net is your best bet. Shooting them tends to make too much of a mess. Different sized nets are desirable here.

If possible, build a simple fence using PVC and netting to crowd the fish to one side, then scoop the ones you wish to harvest. Remember, move very slowly and don't become impatient. If you move quickly, they will also. Assuming you have all different sizes of fish, it is best to harvest the larger ones. They do not grow as fast, they eat more food, and they produce less waste as a ratio to what they eat. If you are growing different types of fish, be aware of their mature sizes which may not be the same as the other species in the tank.

PLANTS

It is wise to plant about a fourth of your crop to start, then another fourth in a couple of weeks, etc. This staggering gives you a steady supply of mature food throughout the growing season.

Using this method, there is less chance of everything perishing at the same time should there be a system failure.

Also, this ensures a steady uptake of nitrates. Once the first group is harvested, replace them with a new round.

Be aware of seasonal changes. Gauge when it is time to introduce a new season crop and keep the process going. Aquaponics can produce food year around when the change of seasons are taken into account.

X. Final Aquaponic Words of Wisdom

- Be aware that when emptying out a fish tank using a water pump, for whatever reason, when you unplug the water pump, or turn off the electricity, this does not stop the water flow. A siphon has been created. Lift the pump out of the water to break the siphon or you may have an almost empty fish tank with a bunch of fish flopping around. Yet another great reason to have off-gassed water on hand.

- You will at several points in time have to stick your hand or entire arm in the fish tank. **DO NOT** slather mosquito repellent or lotion all over your hands and arms before working on the system. It will kill the fish.

- Because a fish has jumped out of the tank and is kinda stiff, lying encrusted in dirt looking at you like a fish-eyed fool does not mean he is dead. He's only partially dead. Give it a light rinse and using your hand, dip the fish back in the tank while moving if forward and backward for a while. This will pass water through its mouth and gills and get it going again. Then release the fish. If this does not work, you can always fish him out later.

- Frozen water bottles are a great way to cool the system during the hot summer months. Throw a few in during the day, and re-freeze them at night.

- If the plants in your Aquaponic raft system are doing great, and then somewhat suddenly cease to look so good, look under the raft to make sure no fish have migrated and under the raft living happily munching the roots. Many times baby fish (called fry) will meander through the plumbing to get away from the larger hungry fish.

- If fish are scratching against the edges or bottom of the fish tank, check for white spots on that fish which are a sign of "ick".

- Broadly, there are two kinds of plastic plant baskets available. Those with a rim at the top, and those without. You lose nothing purchasing those with a rim. Those without a rim are fine for a media-based system (they just sit in the media), but not desirable for a raft system. They tend to fall through the raft holes, especially during ebb and flow cycles.

- Tilapia are Cichlids and therefore semi-aggressive. This means they do not play well with others. Consider giving them their own tank, and using another tank to mix fish like Catfish (bottom feeders) and Blue-gill (middle feeders). This creates living zones. They will all go to the top for food regardless of their inclinations.

Bonus 1: Survival Herb Gardening

Inside Out

INTRODUCTION

In a survival situation, easy access to medical treatment will be limited or unavailable. This is a big issue if you or your family has medical conditions. If any of your family are on daily medication that keeps them alive, we recommend you speak with your physician and try to get extra medication even if it means you must pay for it out of pocket.

With that said nature is wisdom in action. For every problem there is always a solution at the tip of your fingers. The trick lies in knowing where to look.

Herbal medicine was the rule until the beginning of the twentieth century where we jumped in the bandwagon of the chemical miracle and its promises. After one hundred years walking that path, we are starting to realize that it was a good learning experience but not the miracle solution we envisioned.
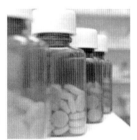
With this information under our belt, we are coming back home, to the roots, with science backing up what ancient medicine knew all along. Cultures like China and India have centuries of experience in herbal medicine.

The approach of herbal medicine to healing is organic and profound. It assumes we are living beings, go figure. The main focus is to keep the "terrain" healthy with all the nutrients it needs in and all the poisons it doesn´t need out. Our body is much more than a bare landscape for the good guys to fight the bad boys. It is a living thing perfectly able to defend itself.

The keyword for herbal medicine is synergism. This is a very important principle stating that the whole is more than the sum of the parts. What does this mean? Plants are formed by different substances and, and these are made out of molecules. Plants usually have what is called active compounds which are the ones conventional medicine tries to isolate, patent and use. The principle of synergism states this is not a good idea: the additional elements in the plant have been wisely added to balance, and help the active compound to create the desired effect without nasty side effects.

There is more to this, latest research is starting to realize that the way the different substances are packaged together also affects the result.

The best way to be healthy is to stay healthy adding herbs and spices to the daily diet is a great and tasty way to stay on the healthy side of the equation. If the herbs are organically grown at home, all the better for your family's survival.

When there is an imbalance, we go after remedies to restore it. Home remedies are usually easy to do and safe for the most part.

In this guide, you will find the basics of natural medicine; how to harvest and conserve plants, how to prepare the medicines. And, we will also give a fast introduction to some of the most common problems and solutions. It is intended as an introduction to the subject, and by no means replaces your doctor's advice. You might want think though about finding a doctor able to catch up with the latest research, which supports the use of herbs and spices in the daily diet as the base for a healthy life. You can also take herbal medicine classes quite affordably on the internet.

This may be a subject your spouse and children may find interesting. If you have started a survival garden, this is a logical accompaniment. Most of the herbs mentioned in this guide can be grown indoors, so you are not shut out of the opportunity if you live in the city and have no ground to plant a garden.

It is not necessary to push this as survival training if your family is still resistant to the idea. Many older children are fans of the Harry Potter books and movies. You could connect training and practice in herbal medicine to that interest.

HOW DOES IT WORK?

Nature uses the same building blocks for all its creations. We are made out of the same substances that plants are made out of, just arranged in a different form.

There is much we still don´t know about the way the chemical processes concatenate inside the body, but thanks to science and old wisdom we have access to the information about how to take care of ourselves. It is important to remember that natural healing means slow and steady. It is not the same as taking a few capsules and feeling better within hours. That is why you will find in all of these guides the advice about getting your family healthy now and maintaining their health. This will increase your chances of surviving in a crisis.

Nature works with bundles, which is something we are only starting to grasp now on the conventional medicine side. For example, bones are mainly made out of calcium; but in the cases where osteoporosis hit, adding more calcium to the diet is usually a very bad idea. Why? Because in most cases what is lacking is magnesium, the glue that keeps the calcium in place, or vitamin D, a very necessary component to have the whole system working.

We are just scratching the surface of how these groups of substances work together, but Nature knows all about it. This is why healing with herbs usually has fewer side effects than their chemical counterparts; the groups are already built in.

When we use only edible plants, fresh or dry, we are on the safe side. When we use different methods to prepare herbal remedies we might break some of the healthy bundles apart, and we need to use due diligence to understand when and how to use them. When preparing healing remedies, we usually also make concentrations of active substances, and the amounts we can use before crossing the dangerous line is different from the original herb.

An example is a remedy known as the Himalayan garlic remedy. It is made out of garlic and vodka, and it is said

to work as a multifunction cleansing and healing remedy. What is the catch? It is made out of a pound of garlic, and double the amount of vodka. Can you imagine if the active elements of a pound of garlic completely infused the vodka? Once it is done, it can only be taken as a couple of drops before meals following a careful schedule; and the whole treatment can only be done once a year. Of course, people with sensibility to alcohol are out, people with stomach issues are out, pregnant woman are out, etc.

Another example is a typical case where our interjection is showing to be very dangerous. Pasteurization of milk appeared as a great solution for the dairy industry, because the natural occurring bacteria in the milk used to spoil it after just a few days destroying the profit. Right now, we almost do not have raw milk for consumption. But, the pasteurization process not only kills bacteria, it also destroys a substance called lactase, necessary to digest the milk sugar lactose. What is the result? Lactose intolerance galore.

ACTIVE INGREDIENTS

It is very well known that certain plants have been used for centuries to treat certain types of illnesses. This last century science is catching up, and now we know which active ingredients can be used for each problem.

Alkaloids

Alkaloids are a diverse group; their common element is to have a molecule with nitrogen (NH2) which makes them pharmacologically active. Different types of alkaloids can be found in different plants; some plants to mention are coffee, tobacco, belladonna, opium. Many of them are toxic in big amounts. Most seem to affect the brain one way or another.

Anthraquinones

This is the active ingredient in plants like rhubarb root and senna known for their laxative properties. The anthraquinones irritate the large intestine causing it to contract and expel its contents. They also soften the stools making the process easier. Due to their irritating properties, they cannot be used regularly. They are usually taken with calmative herbs like ginger or fennel.

Bitters

The bitters are a broad group only connected by the taste. They stimulate secretions in the salivary glands and digestive organs. These secretions aid the appetite and strengthen the digestive process, allowing a better absorption of nutrients. Bitter herbs usually have other active ingredients.

Flavonoids

These components can be found in a wide variety of plants, they have anti-inflammatory properties, and they are good to maintain a healthy circulatory system. Rutin for example, can be found in lemons and strengthens the capillary walls; it is also a strong antioxidant.

Mucilage

They are chains of polysaccharides (big molecules of sugar); they are characterized by their ability to absorb water forming a gel-like substance. The mucilage covers mucous membranes relieving inflammation and soothing irritation. Its action works for respiratory tract, urinary system, and digestive system. The American variation of the elm tree (Ulmus rubra) is a well known mucilage.

Tannins

All plants produce tannins, some more than others. Animals and insects avoid those with large amounts because of its strong pungent taste.

They are astringent. In industry, their ability to contract tissue makes them valuable for curing leather. In the body, the contraction they produce helps to protect the tissue from infections. What tannins do is to bind albumen, a substance found in the mucous membranes and skin.

Black tea has tannins; this is why it can upset the stomach when drinking it alone after fasting.

Volatile Oils

Volatile oils are the ones extracted from plants to make essential oils. Some plants have many. For example the cajuput is known to have over 60 volatile oils. Differ-

ent oils have different properties; some are known for their anti-inflammatory properties, others are antiseptic. Some aid blood circulation, others are diuretic. Usually the volatile oils of the different plants carry the plant therapeutic properties with it.

PLANTING YOUR GARDEN

Finding the right plant we are seeking in the wild – instead of a poisonous cousin- is not that simple. The best way to go is to buy the plants we want to have at our fingertips and care for them. With a well-selected group of plants, we can have the basics covered at home.

You can buy the familiar seed packages at the store, but if you are really serious about a long-term survival situation you ought to consider locating seeds that are not hybridized just like your vegetable seeds. This will give you the ability to collect seeds for succeeding generations of plants. (Hybridized seeds often do not produce viable seeds.)

The selection should include:

- antiseptic plants (thyme for example),
- plants to heal cuts (aloe vera and marigold are good),
- plants to help with upset stomach or irritation (mint works wonders),
- plants to balance mood (lavender flowers can take care of this and more),
- something for detoxification and to boost the immune system (parsley or cilantro does just that).

The plants you choose must work for your location and soil, but for every climate there is a group of plants that will fit the bill. And, if there are no nice looking plants, there surely will be weeds. Dandelion, for example, is a miracle worker in a tiny package.

Once you have your herbs and plants, there are best practices for cutting, storing and different processes to prepare the medicines.

Thyme

Uses: Culinary, herbal medicine.

Function: Strong antibiotic properties, anti-inflammatory.

Plant family: Mint.

Scientific name: Thymus Vulgaris.

Origin: South of Europe.

Botanical info: It is a perennial small shrub with small elongated leaves. It prefers well drained rich soils and warm climates; but can take low temperatures - it can be seen growing wild high in the mountains. Like most herbs, it needs plenty of sun. They grow by seed and root separation. In spring it has small white or purple flowers.

Nutritional facts: According to the USDA recorded values, thyme is a good source of vitamin A, vitamin C, vitamin B-6, iron, manganese, calcium and fiber.

Health benefits: Anti-spasmodic, anti-inflammatory, expectorant, cholagogue and carminative.

Main active ingredients: Thymol (volatile oil). Thymol contains antiseptic and anti-fungal properties. Many Phenolic antioxidants (flavonoids), like zeaxanthin, lutein, pigenin, naringenin, luteolin, and thymonin. Fresh thyme herb is considered to have one of the highest antioxidant levels among herbs.

Culinary uses: Add it to tomato sauce, stew, chicken, soup, shrimp or meats.

Used parts: Leaves, flowers.

Conservation: Let the leaves dry in an airy and dark place. Once dried, put in jars.

Herbal preparation: Thyme is prepared in infusion/tea (leaves), as essential oil (flowers), and as infused oil (leaves).

Aloe Vera

Latin Name: Taraxacum officinale

Part Used: Leaf

Herb Forms : Juice, gel, ointment, powder.

Affects: Integumentary system.

Cautions: Powdered leaf acts as cathartic. Contraindicated during pregnancy and not for long-term use.

Botanical Info: A spiny succulent perennial. The long leaves are thick and full of juice and smooth except for spiny teeth on the margins.

Description: The juice of aloe vera is taken internally for constipation and to soothe ulcers, arthritis, and colitis. A fresh leaf or the juice of aloe vera is applied for burns, sun-burn, poison oak (can be safely used around the eyes), and wounds. As a skin emollient, aloe vera is often an ingredient in cosmetics.

Caution: The resinous layer just beneath the skin contains anthraquinones, which have a strong laxative effect on the bowels.

Aloe Vera has a taste of bitter.

Marigold

Latin Name: Calendula officinalis

Other Names: Pot marigold

Part Used: Flowers

Herb Forms: Tinctures, salves, oils, creams, bulk herb.

Affects: Urinary system, Integumentary system

Cautions: None noted.

Botanical Info: A herb of the daisy family with elongated, tongue-shaped leaves and abundant bright orange flowers. A garden favorite; abundantly reseeds itself.

Description: Calendula is popular in ointments, salves, or

creams for various skin problems, such as eczema, skin rashes, bed sores, diaper rash, varicose veins, bruises, burns, and sore breasts. The tea is used locally for sore throats, slow-healing wounds, and internally for fever and swollen lymph glands. The tea or tincture is beneficial for the healing of ulcers in the digestive tract and to ease gallbladder inflammation and enlarged, sore lymph glands. An extract of calendula flowers (combined with allantoin) was shown to dramatically accelerate the healing of surgically-induced wounds and prevent infection.

Calendula has a taste of spicy, bitter.

Peppermint

Latin Name : Mentha x piperita

Other Names: Mint

Part Used: Leaves

Herb Forms: Teabag, essential oil, capsule (oil), bulk herb.

Affects: Digestive system, Respiratory system.

Cautions: None noted.

Botanical Info: An aromatic perennial in the Mint family with creeping rootstock, dark green opposite leaves, purple stems, and small purple pink or white flowers.

Description : Peppermint leaf and oil (2-4 drops in a cup of warm water, mixed well) are used to counteract nausea and vomiting and to relieve intestinal gas and bowel irritation. Peppermint is also used for biliary disorders, dyspepsia, headache, and fevers and colds. In Europe, enteric- coated capsules of peppermint oil are taken for colitis and irritable bowel syndrome. In Chinese medicine, it is indicated for fever and headaches associated with certain kinds of colds and flu, (wind-heat with yellow or green mucus and fever), and skin lesions.

The classic European cold and flu remedy is made by making a strong infusion with 1 part each of peppermint herb, yarrow tops, and elder flowers and drinking 1-2 cups hot.

Take a hot bath during the time the tea is consumed, wrap up in a sheet, and cover yourself with a sleeping bag--then sweat. This sweating therapy is good for breaking a fever (diaphoretic), releasing heat and toxins from the body. Make sure to replace lost liquids with plenty of herb tea or water.

Peppermint oil in enteric-coated (dissolves in the small intestine) capsules is used today for easing chronic digestive pains and cramping due to gas or irritable bowel syndrome.

Peppermint has a taste of aromatic, spicy.

Lavender

Latin Name: Lavandula officinalis

Part Used: Flowers

Herb Forms: Tincture, bulk herb, essential oil, soap, bath and hair products, and creams.

Affects: Digestive system, Nervous system

Cautions: None noted.

Botanical Info: A small perennial shrub from the Mint family with tall, purple-spiked flowering parts.

Description: Lavender flowers are used to lift the spirits and allay nausea and are said to have a slight sedative quality. Lavender infusion or oil is used for spasms, colic, and neuralgia, internally as well as externally.

Lavender oil is effective topically for burns, and a few drops of it may be added to baths before bedtime for persons with sleep disorders.

Lavender has long been used in traditional medicine for nervous stomach, spasmodic conditions, flatulence, nervous headache, neuralgia, and vomiting.

Lavender has a taste of aromatic, spicy.

Parsley

Latin Name: Petroselinium crispum

Other Names: Garden parsley, cilantro

Part Used: Leaf, Root, Fruits

Herb Forms : Capsule, bulk herb for tea.

Affects: Reproductive system, Digestive system, Urinary system

Cautions: Contraindicated during pregnancy and in cases of inflammatory

kidney disease. Be moderate with fruit preparations.

Botanical Info: A biennial from the Parsley family with fibrous roots and curled, crisped dark green dissected leaves, insignificant greenish flowers,

and plump aromatic fruits. Native to the Mediterranean region.

Description: Parsley's primary uses are as a diuretic, carminative, and emmenagogue. Because it stimulates the elimination of uric acid, parsley is indicated for arthritis and gout. It is taken for lack of appetite, to reduce inflammation, and for urinary tract disorders.

Freshly picked parsley leaves are high in iron content and Vitamin C and are often used as a breath freshener. The roots, seeds, and leaves are used, but the fruits are the most potent diuretic.

Parsley has a taste of sweet, acrid.

Dandelion

Latin Name: Taraxacum officinale

Other Names: Lion's tooth

Part Used: Root, Leaf

Herb Forms: Tincture, capsule, tablet, teabag, bulk herb, powder.

Affects: Endocrine system, Liver

Cautions: The root is contraindicated in cases of bile duct or intestinal blockage and gallbladder inflammation.

Botanical Info: A common plant of the Aster family with single flowering heads full of bright yellow strap-shaped flowers on hollow, single stalks with hairless, large-toothed leaves.

Description: Dandelion root, ubiquitous in lawns and gardens, is widely-used for cooling and cleansing the liver; it is excellent in formulas for hepatitis, cirrhosis, and liver toxicity. It increases the flow of bile and has been used for cholecystitis, gallstones, and jaundice. Dandelion has anti- carcinogenic, estrogen-lowering, and blood cholesterol-lowering capabilities. It also helps with headaches, emotional swings before or during menstruation, acne, red, irritated eyes, mood swings, and other problems related to "liver heat" and is a strong diuretic. In Chinese medicine, dandelion root is taken internally and applied topically for abscesses and nodules. Additionally, it is used to increase lactation and clear liver heat when there are symptoms such as painfully inflamed eyes. Dandelion root tea is also a famous specific for breast cancer but should be taken in conjunction with other blood purifying herbs, such as sarsaparilla, red clover, and burdock root, as well as appropriate immune-strengthening herbal therapy and positive dietary and lifestyle changes.

Dandelion has a taste of bitter, sweet.

STORING YOUR OWN PLANTS

Harvesting

Most herbs are at their best before the flower blooms. This is a bit tricky if you are starting out, so you might want to get to know the particularities of your plants as fast as possible.

Different plants will have different parts that are useful for your purposes. For example, thyme is mostly used for its leaves (for food and natural health), and its flowers are harvested to make essential oils. Dandelion is edible from root to flower, the root makes a good coffee extender, the leaves replace anything you do with spinach – it is bitter though;

the flowers are great additions to salads and they can be used to make syrup and wine.

The best time to harvest leaves and bark is usually the early morning before the sun evaporates the volatile substances on the surfaces. In the case of flowers, they are usually at their best at midday when there is plenty of sun. Roots don´t have a favorite harvesting time, any time will do.

Preparing the Plants

The plants need to be thoroughly cleaned and let dry before storing them. The above ground (aerial) parts usually don´t need washing, but depending on your circumstances you might have to do it. Roots, rhizomes and barks do need to be washed and cleaned of dirt and debris. Use water and a clean sponge or a soft brush to do it.

Once you have all your plants clean, you need to chop the heavier parts – roots and bark, to reduce the size in order to help them dry faster. The aerial parts are usually not cut before drying (to dry thyme tie it in a bundle and hang it upside down in a dark and airy place, do the same with lavender flowers).

To dry your plants look for an airy spot out of the sun. If you can, hang the aerial parts in bundles. In the case of bark or roots, use trays and leave space between the pieces to allow air circulation. Some people take a shortcut and use the oven at a VERY low temperature and with the door open. If you plan to dry your herbs regularly you might want to invest in a food dryer, there are some that work with wood.

You will know if you did it wrong because you will see mold growing. If this happens, accept that you learned something and discard the plant--it is toxic.

Storing the Plants

Hands down, the best receptacles to store your plants are glass jars that are air tight. The next best is a ceramic container, and from there it goes downhill.

Before storing, make sure both your herbs and the jars are perfectly dry. Once you close the lid, if there is humidity in the plants or the jar, the product will be spoiled. If it is kept where it gets sunlight, it will lose potency in just a few months. These warnings should be familiar to you as they applied to extending the shelf life of your survival food storage.

If you store them in the right container and put them in a dark place, they can last several years. They will lose potency nonetheless but much slower. After three or four years, you will need to double or triple the amounts to have the potency of a new preparation. After four years, unless you have no choice, it is probably better to discard it and do a new batch. So, date them as you would any of your survival supplies.

PREPARING HERBAL REMEDIES

There is something that needs to be stressed at this point. Most of the plants used to prepare remedies are edible, but although they are edible in their natural state, the processes to create the remedy might change their composition. In most cases, you create a concentrate of the active substances and lose part of the complementary elements in the process.

This is why - when in doubt - the diagnoses have to be done by a professional, whether it is a naturopath or a conventional doctor. Once a plant is transformed in a remedy, quantities matter. Self-medication can be as dangerous with herbal remedies as self-medication of drugs. On the other hand, nobody will know your body as yourself if you pay attention; it is a delicate balance, use due diligence and make safe choices. This is one reason you should learn everything you can ahead of time and practice preparing the various forms used for treatment.

Your remedies will take different forms. The best choice will depend on the nature of the plant and the purpose.

Infusion

Basically, an infusion is a tea. Bring water to boil (or almost), remove from the heat and pour over your herbs.

When an infusion is created for healing purposes, the steeping time is about 30 minutes. The amount of herb used will depend on the potency you seek. It is usually one teaspoon per cup  of water when the herbs are dry, and double if the herbs are fresh. In the case of fresh herbs, break them up in a mortar to increase the efficiency of the hot water drawing out the juices. After the appropriate amount of time, the herbs are removed, and the liquid is ready to drink or store.

Infusions are the best options for herbs when you want to extract water soluble substances and the plant is delicate.

Cold Infusion

In some cases, you don´t heat the water to make an infusion. This is used for example when you want to extract soluble elements from bark or roots in cold to avoid losing delicate substances. A typical procedure punctures the bark and pours water in the created space. After a couple of days, that water contains the soluble elements. This is used with quassia amara, similar to tea tree, for stomach problems.

A completely different procedure, but still a cold infusion is to put garlic and honey with water in a jar and bury it underground for a couple of months. The result was used by some nomad groups in ancient times as cold and flu remedy.

Decoction

Decoction is a fancy word to make a soup. It is usually done with harder parts of the plants - like roots or bark. Put your plants in cold water and bring it to a boil. The boiling times are between 10 and 30 minutes depending on the sizes of the pieces and how hard they are.

After the boiling time, take it out; leave it to cool, extract the plants and use or store. It is a good procedure to extract minerals.

Tincture

Tinctures are used to extract oils, or anything alcohol soluble. The usual choice for homemade remedies is vodka or food grade alcohol. Some grandma remedies use wine.

The procedure is simple, just add the plants broken up in a mortar to a jar - if you are using fruits you can leave them in pieces, pour the alcohol making sure it covers them completely, and leave it in a dark place for at least two weeks. You can shake it from time to time to help the process. If you use fruits, you will notice they swallow, absorbing part of the liquid. Make sure there is always enough alcohol to cover the plants completely; otherwise, they might be colonized by fungus.

After the waiting time is up, extract the liquid making sure you press the plants or fruit to recover part of the absorbed alcohol as well.

Alcohol is very volatile, and light affects the tincture efficiency. So it is better to keep them in tight-lidded jars of dark glass in a dark cool place.

Poultice

Poultices are applied topically. They consist of applying the plants right over the skin or using gauze to make a "pouch". A typical case is aloe leaves for healing burns or small cuts. In this case, the leaves are cut open, and the gel the plants contain is applied directly on the skin.

Syrup

Only Nature knows why, but many healing plants are very bitter. To make them easier to take – especially when kids of all ages are involved, infusions and decoctions can be cooked with honey or sugar to make healing syrups.

Syrups are also made from tinctures when wine is involved. A typical cough remedy is made out of wine, honey, cinnamon and a pinch of ginger. The ingredients are boiled and the preparation reduced until it produces a syrup.

Infused Oil

Infused oils can be created either at room temperature or with the application of heat. The plant is put in oil and left to macerate for a couple of weeks. After the time elapses, the solid parts are strained out leaving clean and aromatic oil. Infused oils are great to use on a daily basis for cooking as in the case of herbs and spicy veggies (like garlic or onions). Or, they can be infused with flowers to be used topically. A typical case is lavender infused oil.

Ointment

Ointments are similar to infused oils, but they use substances that are solid at room temperature. The consistency can be hard or soft. For hard ointments, a combination that works as a base is coconut oil and bee wax. For softer ointments, the coconut oil can be replaced by olive oil. Ointments are usually used topically.

The procedure to make them consists of heating the base oils to melt, adding the herbs, cooking at low temperature for about 15 minutes and straining it before it cools down. After it cools down, it will solidify again.

CONCLUSION

It is not alarmist or paranoid to think that in an emergency medical treatment might not be available. Depending on where you live, the hospital may be too far away in a crisis. Not only that, the events of Hurricane Katrina taught all of us concerned with survival that hospitals quickly become overwhelmed and begin turning all but the most severely injured people away. They ran out of drugs because of the influx of the injured.

It becomes a point of self-reliance. If you can get by on knowledge of basic herbal medicine until things return to normal without placing your family at risk, why take the chance of being attacked on the trip to the hospital, especially if you are only going to be turned away.

The likelihood of needing medical treatment is great depending on the circumstances. Obviously, you and your family will be doing unfamiliar things that can lead to injuries, and changes in the environment may contribute to medical conditions.

Another argument for learning about basic herbal medicine and first aid that you can do yourself is that it is a very valuable skill. If you or a member of your family becomes proficient in herbal or alternative methods of healing, you are going to be perceived as a valuable addition to any group.

Even if you do not have a group of fellow survivalists that you established before the disaster or crisis, eventually survivors will begin to band together to barter and trade. Human nature fosters the formation of groups and communities because the load is lightened by many hands.

Bonus 2: How To Build a Wicking Bed System

Another water conserving gardening technique

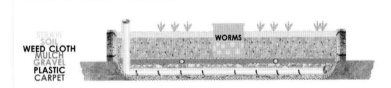

INTRODUCTION

With the ever changing climate and demands on water supply, it is more important than ever to look for simple, yet effective ways to adapt and be diverse when being your own provider of food.

As with many other things in life, it is not kosher to put all your eggs in one basket. This is especially important as it applies to growing your own food sustainably.

Even though standard gardening techniques have been proven over the years and may at times appear to be the more stable, in excessive hot or cold climates or years with more extreme weather, it is subjected to many factors that can result in destruction of your entire crop and will most likely require more resources than other techniques in the long run. This is just one very important reason to diversify.

Besides diversifying for the security or piece of mind, it can be really fun to try new methods and techniques that can save you time, resources and money.

Not to mention you may be surprised at the results.

One of my favorite techniques that I like to use to diversify my food supply with is a wicking bed, or what I like to call my "set it and almost forget it" gardening method. Why do I call is my "set it and forget it" method.. well, even in the hottest of hot Texas summer weeks, I can get away with only watering my garden once a week plus like most raised bed gardens it is virtually weedfree.

Only having to water once a week is great for many reasons… are on water restrictions due to drought conditions in your area, maybe it is hard to get water to your garden, what if you have to go out of town for the weekend or heck you can't bear to make it outside because it is still 100 degrees at 9 at night or maybe you just plain forget, your plants are will still be alive and happy.

Well, can't I just have a timer with a drip irrigation system?

Yes... that is a great way to reduce water needs... but do you really want to have to deal with all those little irrigation pieces and what if the timer fails? Don't get me wrong, I put soaker/drip hoses in my traditional garden beds with mulch and it reduces the gardens water needs too.... but it doesn't give your plants a continuous supply of water and nutrients like a wicking bed can.

So what is heck is a wicking bed anyway?

In short, a wicking bed is a self-contained raised bed with a built-in reservoir that supplies water by "wicking" from the bottom up through a porous material such as landscaping fabric or weed block.

See the illustration below:

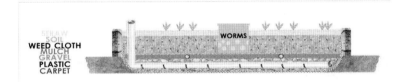

Figure 1: Side view showing layers of a wicking bed

As the soil located above the weed cloth gets dry, the moisture is drawn or "wicked" up into the soil from the gravel based water reservoir. The reservoir results in less frequent watering, minimizes evaporation and has shown to have a reduction of water usage by up to 50%, as well as increased production and quality.

Wicking beds will typically last for a couple years, allowing you to water only once a week during summer or warmer months and once every few weeks the rest of year.

You may be thinking... this concept isn't new, and you're right. It has just started to gain in popularity due to concerns over water conservation and places that have issues due to sever climates. You may have also seen premade pots with self-watering systems; well these are essential media free wicking beds.

Now you are thinking, why shouldn't I make all my gardens wicking beds?

Well, wicking beds actually work best with leafy and top fruiting plants and veggies. Your root vegetables should still be planted in a regular style gardening bed, even though I have planted stubby varieties of carrots with great success.

Here is a quick side by side of the advantages and disadvantages of wicking beds.

Advantages	Disadvantages
Water-efficient: *Watering from the bottom up prevents evaporation of surface water.*	**Not suitable for all veggies:** *Root vegetables are not recommend for wicking beds.*
Self Watering: *Saves you time from watering every day on hot weeks. A wicking bed should irrigate itself for about a week.*	**Increased Cost:** *Material costs are slightly more and there is a little more prep than a traditional raised garden.*
Drainage system: *Built in overflow in the event of a large downpour.*	**Freeze in colder months:** *Additional precautions may need to taken because it is a raised bed with a water reservoir.*
Warms up quicker and easy to attach cold frames.	

If you really think about it, the advantages of a wicking bed far outweigh any disadvantages that you would experience. As for cost being a disadvantage, I think you would find that the money you would save on water would offset the initial cost of materials. And remember, I am trying to stress the importance of diversity and share alternative water conserving methods for growing your own food, because I know one size doesn't fit all.

Now let's get to the nitty gritty and start building. Happy wicking!

HOW TO MAKE A WICKING BED GARDEN

A wicking bed system is a way of growing plants where water is wicks up from an underground water reservoir resulting in improved production while minimizing water usage.

In this how-to we are going to cover how to make 4 ft. x 8 ft. wicking bed garden.

Materials

2 - 2x12x12 *(cut each board into 1 - 4ft and 1 - 8ft piece)*

Reminent carpet or other suitable material to cover area *(to protect plastic liner)*

10 ft - 3 or 4 inch inch dia. pvc pipe

1 - elbow to fit pipe

2 - caps to fit ends of pipe *(or make)*

1 - roll black plastic to cover area

1 - roll weed block to cover area

8 ft - 1 inch pvc pipe

Wood/decking screws *(9 in)*

1- 4x4x8 *(cut 0 pieces the width of the 12x12)*

12 bags gravel/river pebbles *(enough for 4 to 6 inches deep - approx 1/2 cu yard)*

3 bags of revitalize/compost

Mulch *(enough for 0 to 2 inches deep - approx 3 - 2cu ft bags)*

Soil *(from an organic garden)*

Optional Items

1 - bucket with lid for compost/worm bin

Bale of straw or additional mulch for topping

Tools

Circular Saw *(to cut wood)*

Level

Drill *(electric)*

Drill bits *(various sizes)*

Hole cutters or paddle drill bit *(7 7/0 in to 7 7/8 in for the 1 inch pvc pipe)*

Measuring tape

Staple gun

Hammer

Shovel

Wheel barrel

Scissors

Utility knife

Hacksaw *(to cut pvc pipe)*

Old tomato cage, wire fence, *(or something to use to sift/ break up dirt removing rock and large clods)*

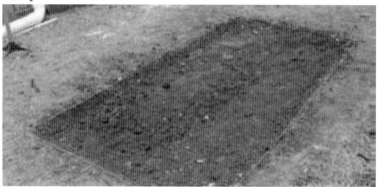

1. Determine an ideal location for your wicking bed garden and mark off the area.

2. For a good supporting base to the raised bed, dig down about 4 to 6 inches. This provides a good basin and also minimizes the weight of the gravel pushing on the wood frame.

3. Layout your reminent carpet over your marked off area, measure and cut to size.

4. Allow a few inches on each side so that it will fold inside the frame *(see below)*.

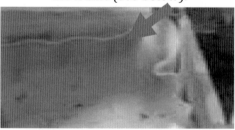

Carpet should be top down, this helps protect the plastic from punctures. Other suitable material can be used. Remember this area is not going to contact the soil.

Prep Irrigation Pipe

1. Drill holes in one side of the pipe approximately every 6 inches *(you can also make slots instead of holes if you don't have a drill bit)*.

2. Attach the 90 degree elbow to one end of the pipe. Measure and cut the pipe to the approximate length of the bed. For a more precise measurement, place the pipe with the elbow attached inside the wood frame before cutting *(remember to accommodate an inch or two for the rug)*.

3. If you purchased a cap, cap off the cut end of the pipe. In this example, we use left over foam insulation from our raft aquaponic system.

4. Cut the foam and fit it into the end of the pipe.

5. Cover with an old t-shirt and zip tie the shirt over the end.

Wood Frame

1. Cut each 2x12x12 into 1 - 4ft long piece and 1 - 8ft long piece

2. Cut the 4x4 into 4 - 1ft long pieces

3. Attach one end of the 2x12 to the 4x4 with 3 - 3 inch screws.

4. Continue to layout the boards such that the 2-long boards and 2-short boards are parallel to one another forming a rectangle. Placing a 4x4 in each corner. Attach each 2x12 to the 4x4s in the corners.

5. Once the frame is complete, place the frame over the marked out area. Fold the carpet so that it is inside the frame. Check to see the PVC piece is a snug fit. You want to ensure water is distributed the full length of the bed.

6. Use a level and check to make sure the frame is sitting fairly level on all sides.

Adding the Layers

1. Cut plastic to size. Similar to the carpet, allow for extra on each side.

2. Lay the plastic over the carpet.

3. Tack the plastic to the frame with a staple gun or other suitable tack to hold the plastic in place. Does need to be perfect.

4. Lay the large PVC pipe toward the center of the framed area. Check to see if fairly level and/or slighting toward the capped end. (you want to ensure the water flows the length of the bed) Also make sure the holes are toward the bottom.

5. Start laying down the gravel/rock. The gravel should be about 4 to 6 inches deep, almost to the top of the pipe *(in the wicking bed we used Vigor decorative river pebble).*

6. Add layer of mulch, also 4 to 6 inches. To ensure the pipe is covered. This will break down over time and add additional nutrients to the garden *(the irregular pieces help hold more water.)*

7. Position 2 - 1- inch PVC pipes with holes *(about 6 inches apart)* on one side, equal distant from the ends. Drill a hole *(just large enough for the pipes to slide through)* for each pipe in the long side of the frame.

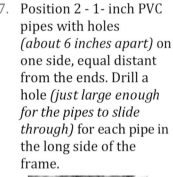

These pipes will act as an overflow letting you know when your reservoir is full of water.

8. Slide the pipes through the holes. One end should be flush with the inside of the frame while the other sticks out a few inches.

Make sure the holes face down.

Soil Prep

1. Ideally, take soil from an existing organic garden. Remove any rocks and break up any clods. You can use old fencing as a grate to sift the soil.

2. Lay down a piece of plastic. This is to help keep your soil free of debris, grass, weed, etc. and provide an easy surface to mix.

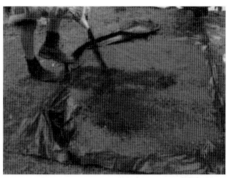

3. Dump a full wheel barrel of soil on the plastic and add compost revitalizer. In this example we used Lady Bug brand revitalizer compost. There are many other great brands out there, use what is local or available to you.

4. Mix the two as you go for a better, more equal distribution *(for this area, we used 3 bags).*

8. Lay down and tack the weed barrier plastic to the frame with a staple gun or other suitable tack to hold the plastic in place.

NOTE: Don't use regular plastic, the water needs to be able to "wick" through to the roots of your plants.

9. Position your compost/ worm bin.

10. Dump the blended soil into the prepped bed on the weed block material. Fill up to about 1 inch from the top.

11. Break up a bail of straw and cover the bed. (if you don't have straw to use as a mulch you can use whatever you have).

Now your bed is complete and ready for planting!

TEST YOUR SYSTEM

Fill the reservoir. Allow the water to run until you see water coming out the pipes on the side. Initially this will take the longest... approximately 10 minutes, before water comes out the overflow pipes. Because all the of material is new, you may have to top off the water gets absorbed into the mulch, soil, etc. You can check levels by looking down the pipe.

After the initial setup, you should only need to water about once a week.

Also, to protect your plants you may want to make a shade structure over the new bed.

Bonus 3: Hoop House Magic

An inexpensive flexible structure

INTRODUCTION

Often time's seasonal changes and weather conditions are a major concern because it can wreak havoc on your crops impacting yields. Wouldn't it be nice to have a greenhouse type structure for food production year round, without being expensive or permanent?

Introducing hoop houses (also known as polytunnels or monkey huts), an inexpensive, quick to assemble, portable structure designed to withstand strong winds, rain and more. This simple, semi-circular structure allows the suns warmth to build up heat much faster while being able to easily control temperature, humidity and ventilation. As a result, commercial growers around the world have been using these types of structures for years to significantly increase production and yields.

If Commercial Growers Use It... Why Not You?

Hoop houses are a great, naturally flexible companion to any food growing system because they can be sized to meet your needs with just a few components you can pick up at any local hardware store. These structures can typically be assembled in about an hour and help protect your food production systems from excessive rain, intense heat, wind, frost and even help extend your warm growing season.

So, What Makes Up a Hoop House?

The materials of a hoop house are quite simple and if you bought everything new for a 10x12 ft structure, would probably cost about $200 but can easily be less if you reuse or recycle materials you may have lying around the house.

A basic hoop house structure is made up of Schedule 40 PVC (3/4" to 1 ¼"), T connectors, X connectors, rebar, Duct Tape, rope/bungie cords/zip ties, and a cover (for gardening, probably a 6 mil clear plastic would work for winter applications, or sun/shade cloth for summer applications in warmer climates).

If you feel like getting a little fancy and want to make your structure more permanent, you may add bricks or cinder blocks, some wood and screws to make a door and frame around the base.

As always be creative and resourceful, that is what makes projects like these fun and rewarding.

LET'S BUILD IT!

In this example we are going to get a little fancy and build a semi-permanent hoop house structure to protect an aquaponic system during the winter months. Below is the basic overhead structure of what we will be covering.

You will see we are going to construct a 10 x 15 ft structure that is about seven and a half feet tall in the center. To scale for your needs, a good rule of thumb is for every 5 ft, put a support or rib. If you want it stronger, put them closer together.

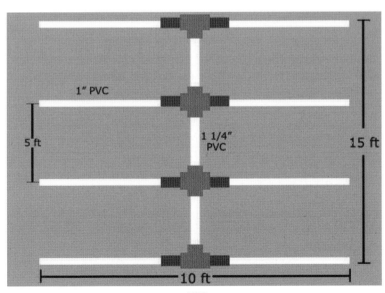

MATERIAL LIST

3 – 10 ft x 1 ¼" schedule 40 PVC

8 – 10 ft x 1" schedule 40 PVC

2 – 1 ½" T – Connectors

2 – 1 ½" X –Connectors

8 – 2' x ½" rebar

Box of 6 mil 20 x 100 ft. Clear Plastic Sheeting

Nylon rope or bungies

Duct Tape

Some Extras for a base and door

2x4s, 2x2's ,1x4's for the door frame.

Decking screws, nails or staples

TOOLS

Sledge Hammer (to knock in rebar) Rubber Mallet (just in case you need to tap PVC together)

Utility Knife/Scissors

Tape Measure

PVC cutter/Hack Saw/ or Circular saw to cut PVC (and wood if using it)

Drill (optional for the extras)

Shovel (optional for the extras or smoothing out footprint area)

SETUP/PREP

1. Cut one of the 10 ft. x 1 ¼" PVC pipes into half and cut each of those pieces in half again. You will have 4 – 2 ½ ft. pieces. Take 2 of the 2 ½ ft pieces and wrap duct tape around the middle until there is enough duct tape to make a T – connector fit snug. See images below.

    Repeat the process for the remaining 2 pieces, now for the 2 X-Connectors.

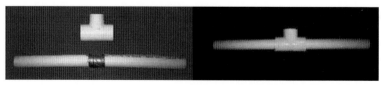

2. Layout 2 – 10 ft. x 1" PVC pipes. Measure out 15" from one end of each pipe. Wrap the pipes with duct tape just to the inside of the 15" mark. Use enough duct tape until the pipe fits snug into the connector pieces created in Step 1. This makes one support or rib.

   Repeat this process three more times for the remaining T - connector and 2 – X connectors. You should end up with 4 - 20 ft. long pieces.

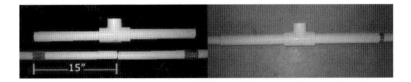

3. Take the remaining 2 – 10 ft. x 1 1/4" PVC pipes and cut in half. You will have 4 – 5 ft. pieces. Take 3 of the 5 ft. pieces and wrap duct tape around both ends of each piece such that the ends fit snug in the T and X connectors. These pieces will make up the spine or center support along the length of the structure. Each end will slide into a T or X connector, holding the ribs in place.

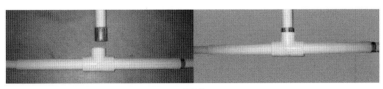

ASSEMBLY

Now that we have all the component pieces, we can start assembling the structure.

1. Mark out the area for the 10' x 15' footprint. Because we are making it a little more permanent, we are digging a groove for the 2x4 base to rest in.

2. Down the length or long side of the area, measure every 5 feet and hammer in a piece of rebar. Each piece of rebar should be about one foot deep into the ground.

3. Take a rib with the X-Connector and slide one end of it onto one of the center pieces of rebar. Pull the other end of the rib down, arching it to slide the other end onto the rebar on the opposite size of the area. Repeat this process with the remaining ribs.

4. Connect the ribs together by placing the 3 - 5 ft. x 1 ¼" pieces in to the X and T connectors to create the center support or spine.

5. Once the ribs are connected to the spine, use nylon rope or bungie cords to secure the ribs to the spine. This will help keep the frame from separating and more stable.

6. After the frame is secure, to make your hoop house a

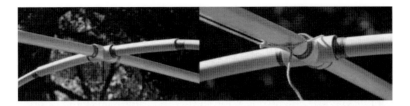

little more fancy, you can cut to size a frame with 1x4's to make a door like in the frame picture show above.

7. Now the frame is ready for the cover. Unroll the clear plastic the full length of the frame. Unfold the plastic sheeting around the frame until it is completely covered, then cut the plastic from the roll. This process may take a few extra hands.

8. Now secure the plastic cover to the frame. In our example, we are using a spare 2x2's to wrap the bottom of the plastic and nail it to the 2x4 frame base. You could also use tie wraps, bungies or what you have handy to secure the plastic to the frame.

Just put any finishing touches you like, and your hoop house is complete.

VARIATIONS, UPGRADES AND TIPS

Like I mentioned in the intro, you could leave the ends open and use shade/sun cloth as the cover. This would provide a great shelter if you have strong sun exposure, preventing your plants from being scorched in the summer.

Don't have enough space in the garage, a little hoop house could easily solve your space issues to store your lawn mower or garden tools, even recreation vehicles or bikes.

Maybe you need a quick shelter for a day at the park or tail-gating, you can use a 10x20 ft. tarp with bungies to make a quick portable shade area.

Is it a little stuffy inside? Adding a fan can easily help with circulation. Fans are often used in hoop houses and greenhouses to help regulate temperature. Or even positioning from North to South vs. East to West, could give you better ventilation.

If you are really planning on using it for a more permanent application and not for a portable or temporary/seasonal solution, you may want to invest in a higher quality UV cover and/or adding a little foundation depending on what you plan to use it for. Really sky's the limit on what you can do.

A Hoop House is a magical, multi-functional structure! Happy Hoop Hooping!